# INANNA RETURNS

By V.S. Ferguson

# INANNA RETURNS

Part I
*The Family of Anu*

Part II
*Melinar and the Multidimensional Selves*

By V.S. Ferguson

Edited by Tera Thomas
Designed by The Ferguson Company
Seattle, Washington

Thel Dar Publishing Company
Seattle, Washington
1995

# INANNA RETURNS

Part I: The Family of Anu
Part II: Melinar and the Multidimensional Selves

For information contact
Thel Dar Publishing Co.
10002 Aurora Ave. N., #3392
Seattle, Washington 98133-9334

Cover and book design
by Barb Ferguson and The Ferguson Company
Seattle, Washington.

Stars cover photo by Jack B. Newton/Masterfile

ISBN 0-9647276-1-7

✻

*This book
is dedicated
to all those
who long
for freedom.*

# CONTENTS

# ACKNOWLEDGMENTS

As I was writing *Inanna Returns*, I began to feel as if I were out on a vast ocean in a tiny boat, and the people who loved me enough to read my first drafts became my compass and lighthouse on that ocean.

So, I thank my dear friend Anne for caring enough to tackle my first rough draft, for having the courage to tell me the truth and give me structure.

Without Tera Thomas' gift for editing, this book would never have been. Inanna's undoubted assistance, synchronicity, and the planet Jupiter brought us together, while a growing friendship and love sculpted the book. Tera, I am grateful to your Mars in Virgo, your spiritual depth and your boundless heart.

I thank my husband for his humor, his photography, his editing, and his help with "my science"! I love you, Charles.

I also thank Barb Ferguson, my art director, for being what she is as well as for her creativity and inspiration. And Pat Welch, for her essential proofreading.

Thank you to Quentin, my favorite graduate of the Star Fleet Academy, for encouraging me when I needed it; to Anthony for reminding me to remember; thanks also to Suzette, and to my Jenny in England for standing by me; and to Debbi and Nicole for reading *Inanna Returns* so lovingly. Last but not least, I thank my faithful Rhiannon for staying so close, and my beloved Bear.

*Inanna Returns* is loosely based on four sources: the Hindu epic, *The Mahabharata*, as translated by J.A.B. van Buitenen; the works of Zecharia Sitchin, especially *The 12th Planet* and *The Wars of Gods and Men*; the Sumerian translations of the hymns and stories of Inanna, *Inanna, Queen of Heaven and Earth*, by Diane Wolkstein and Samuel Noah Kramer; and a book entitled *The Greatest Story Never Told*, by Lana Corrine Cantrell. I am indebted to all four of these sources as well as many others, especially Doris Lessing for her *Briefing for a Descent into Hell* and her series of science fiction novels, *Canopus in Argos—Archives*.

*The Mahabharata* is the most wonderful book I have ever read. J.A.B. van Buitenen's recent translation is filled with descriptions of space ships, flying celestial cities, radiation weapons, and beings whose adventures defy the imagination. The idea of the "gods" incarnating in the bodies of humans is also expressed in *The Mahabharata*.

In 1990, I read the first three books in the Sitchin series. Part I of *Inanna Returns* springs from my own imagination, but is generally based on Mr. Sitchin's scholarship in these books, for which I am very grateful. As I read *The Wars of Gods and Men*, I found myself carried into Inanna's being, feeling as if I were her, vividly experiencing the scenes of her life. I remembered Nibiru, saw myself as a child there and felt I knew all of Inanna's family intimately. I knew what motivated them and how they felt. I loved them, especially Ninhursag. In my mind, I stood beside the pyramid, striking it with my weapon, and cursing Marduk. I could see Sargon and I knew Inanna's feelings for him. I even purchased a necklace of lapis lazuli.

For me, Inanna's life was like one long exciting movie, and a little bewildering. I have never really known why Inanna's story affected me so profoundly, but eventually it found its way into this book. Inanna shared her life with me in a way that brought me adventure, excitement, confusion, and wisdom. I hope *Inanna Returns* will do the same for you. I know she wants me to bring you this gift, to tell her side of the story.

I thank Zecharia Sitchin, J.A.B. van Buitenen, and all the others who inspired this book for their diligent research, hard work, and imagination. I thank Inanna for her friendship, and her love. She is so lovable.

V.S. Ferguson, 1995

# INTRODUCTION

*by Tera Thomas*

I have long known the stories of our Pleiadian ancestors, the gods who manipulated our DNA, who used us as
workers, and kept us from the secrets of who we really are
to benefit themselves. I had read about them, heard about
them, and edited long passages about them in the Pleiadean
books, *Bringers of the Dawn and Earth*. I felt I really knew
these stories. So, when Susan Ferguson called to ask me
if I would be interested in editing *Inanna Returns*, I almost
said, "Oh, no, not more god stories!" But, something inside
of me said, "Don't be so quick, there is a gift in this for
you." I do listen to my inner guidance; besides, I really
liked Susan, and I was ready for a project, so I said I'd like
to read her draft.

Susan sent me Part I of her book. It was a quick read,
witty and well told, and it pushed my buttons. Through the
voice of Inanna, the gods were presented in a down-to-
Earth, realistic way. They were selfish and annoying,
behaving like people I'd met before, people I didn't want to
hang out with. I complained to Susan, "Inanna is so spoiled
and headstrong and heedless of the consequences of her
actions, and she's supposed to be a goddess, after all!" Susan
laughed and said, "Exactly! The gods have been perpetual
adolescents, spoiled and selfish brats who get whatever
they want or they fight. It's hard to believe that we could
give our power away to someone so ordinary and greedy,
and yet we consistently do it over and over again."

You know how you can hear something so many
times and think you really understand it, then someone can
say one little thing that maybe you've heard before, but for

some reason you hear it differently than you ever did, and that little thing can change your whole perspective? Susan's words brought a big realization to me: these gods are real people, manipulating us to believe that they're gods. And since I had believed these characters were gods and was now angry because they weren't behaving in the way I expected gods to behave, did that mean I was still giving my power away to them, expecting them to be more knowing, more compassionate than an everyday human— namely, me? Did I still have this big gap in my consciousness, separating god and human into two completely different categories?

I read the book again, with new eyes, and this time I felt the story in the core of my being. I was overwhelmed with a feeling of love and respect for Inanna, whose voice rang so true as she told her tales. She was telling her story exactly as it happened. She knew that she and her family members were self-centered and spoiled, that they had caused a lot of damage to the humans and the Earth. By not glossing over or attempting to justify their actions, Inanna was accepting responsibility for what they had created, and she was here to heal it.

In very simple, easy-to-understand language, Inanna brought the gods into my life as real people that I could feel and understand. The stories were no longer just myths to me; my latent memories were jogged, and I knew Anu's family as my family. I realized that Inanna was doing the same thing I've been doing in my life, going into her past to heal her wounds and evolve herself. The gods were suddenly decanonized, demystified, and I *knew* them.

As I was working on Part I of the book, Susan was writing Part II and sending it to me. I got really excited about how the second part of the book continued the saga.

The gods were updated, twentieth-century characters attempting to heal the wounds they had created by actually incarnating into human form to activate the latent genes, and to bring back the knowledge that they had worked so hard to repress. And it became clear that they had done their work of "disconnecting" us so well that rectifying the past has not been an easy task for any of them.

I have grown to know Inanna well, and to love her deeply. I feel her presence with me often. I trust the truth and clarity in her, and I believe in her sincere desire to heal her family's selfish and unthinking deeds. I have also grown to love Susan very much, and I thank her for having the courage to bring Inanna through to tell her story, and for her diligent research to get the historical facts right.

I have loved working on this book. It has been a powerful experience for me. I saw so many areas where I was still programmed to believe things that did not serve me. I understood, and deeply felt, my link to these gods, and I claimed my heritage as one of them in a way I had not done before. In her own candid style, Inanna shares her wisdom and insight to bridge the gap between the gods and the humans. She emphasizes a simple truth, a very important truth: We are the gods, we do have the knowledge and the power, it's in our DNA, it's only been suppressed and latent in our genes, but it's there. We only need to believe it to activate it.

Tera Thomas
February, 1995
Pittsboro, North Carolina

# CAST OF
# CHARACTERS AND PLACES

NIBIRU: an artificial planet, home to Inanna's family.

ANU: Inanna's great-grandfather, ruling Lord of Nibiru and head of the family dynasty.

ANTU: wife/sister of Anu; great-grandmother of Inanna.

NINHURSAG: daughter of Anu and a Pleiadian physician. Herself a physician and a brilliant geneticist who created a race of workers, the Lulus. Head of all medical facilities on Terra.

ENKI: son of Anu and Id (a Princess of the Dragon People); father of Marduk, Nergal, Dumuzi, and countless others.

NINKI: primary spouse of Enki, but not the only mother of his multitudinous offspring.

ENLIL: son of Anu and Antu; legitimate heir to the throne of Nibiru.

NINLIL: wife of Enlil.

NANNAR: father of Inanna; son of Enlil and Ninlil.

NINGAL: mother of Inanna; wife of Nannar.

UTU: the first-born twin brother of Inanna; son of Nannar and Ningal.

NINURTA: son of Ninhursag and Enlil.

ERESHKIGAL: half-sister of Inanna; daughter of Nannar.
NERGAL: husband of Ereshkigal; son of Enki.

DUMUZI: Inanna's first husband; son of Enki.

GESHTINANNA: Dumuzi's sister.

MARDUK: son of Enki.

NINGISHZIDDA: son of Enki and Ereshkigal.

SARGON: one of Inanna's favorite husbands.

GILGAMESH: an illegitimate grandson of Utu who rejects
Inanna's sexual advances.
ENKIDU: friend to Gilgamesh.

MATALI: friend to Inanna; pilot for Enki.
TARA: Matali's wife, one of the Snake People, and Inanna's
best friend.

THE EKUR: the Great Pyramid at Giza.

I

# INANNA SPEAKS

*I, Inanna, am so loved.*
*In many ways, I am love itself.*

We as Pleiadians have always known that love is the essence of creation. All we have ever been is love; love of adventure, love of power, and love of play. This is the story of my family, the family of Anu, who came to your planet from the Pleiades over 500,000 Earth years ago. And as you will see, our story is your story as well, because in our laboratories, my family created your species as it now exists. We were never truly superior to you, only vastly more experienced. My family had been playing in the universe long before we came to Earth. You were our genetic experiment on the periphery of this galaxy.

Let us go back to the beginning. Time is the playing field of the gods, and whose time shall we use, yours or ours? In actuality time does not exist, but it is useful because if one does not draw some boundaries, everything merges.

Thought is projected into space through the infinite varying frequencies of time. There are a multitude of time frequencies, and Earth time is quite different from time as we experience it. From the human perspective, it seems as though we live forever, which makes it quite easy for us to play with Earth's inhabitants.

Because we created the human race in its present form without completely activating your DNA, it never occurred to us that you would ever be more than our playthings, or that you were good for anything more than doing chores such as cooking and cleaning and mining gold. We considered Earth a remote mining operation. We began to teach our humans, and we named them the Lulus. Because we so enjoyed playing with our Lulus, we became fondly attached to them and began to interbreed with them. We fell in love with our own creation.

But we could not stop fighting among ourselves. The Lulus worshipped us as gods, a practice we did not discourage, and we sent them into battle to fight and die for us like pawns in a chess game. They were more than willing to face death just to please us, and we saw them as a renewable resource because we could always create more.

Then we made the error of using the Great Radiation Weapon, the Gandiva. As a result, waves of deadly radiation flowed out into the solar system, out into the galaxy, and attracted the attention of the Council of the Intergalactic Federation. Apprehensive of our reckless behavior, they interfered. They would say "intervened." My family had been so busy fighting, competing, and playing that we had completely forgotten about that nuisance Council. After all, Earth was ours.

The Council members argued that many had colonized Earth before us, and that we had broken the Law of

Prime Creator by endangering other worlds with our marvelous weapons. They also accused us of altering the genetic capacities of the human species, thereby depriving them of the ability to evolve. They charged us with breaking the Law of Non-Interference. Enmeshed in our own problems, we thought it was none of their business. Our family, the family of Anu, was at war, brother against brother.

We did not consider the Council of the Intergalactic Federation so terribly important, not important at all—until we found ourselves surrounded by *The Wall*. Not a real wall like a brick wall, this was an invisible frequency wall, and consequently everything began to change for us. The magic went completely out of our lives; there was no spark, no movement. Life became too solid and dense; it ceased its flow. The Goddess of Wisdom was about to teach us something we had forgotten, or perhaps not yet even begun to learn.

At first we were confused by our boredom, as we had never experienced it before, and we did not like it. We became irritable, almost human, and we certainly didn't like that. We had been eternally expanding and exploring the Universe, easily creating, and having fun. Our lives had been exciting with the infinite power available to us, and then this perplexing state of stagnation fell over us. We had stopped evolving. Erected to teach us by experience what we had done to the Lulus on Earth, The Wall was the discipline our own actions had drawn into our existence.

We could not believe that we had actually stopped evolving. Reluctantly, we approached the Council to ask questions designed to make us look wise, to conceal that we had no idea what was happening to us. They knew anyway. Perhaps they are more advanced than we are, but we are not comfortable with such a depressing thought.

The Council carefully explained to us that we would have to give our earthlings the very same powers that we possess! They informed us that we were responsible for what we had created. What nonsense! We could not accept this. Can you imagine what a nuisance it would be if your pets became your equals? They might begin to talk and even tell you what they wanted for dinner. Where would it end, with a four-course dinner with chocolate truffles for dessert?

We flew home annoyed. Naturally, as was our way, we quarreled among ourselves. Some imagined the Federation was conspiring with our enemies. Others thought the Council obviously wanted Earth for itself. The Sirians had been members longer than we Pleiadeans, or perhaps it was the Arcturians. A few of us of us took it personally, blaming each other. We were a fractious family indeed.

We attempted to dissolve The Wall by performing an enormous ritual sacrifice, quite lovely and grisly actually, to the satisfaction of all those who consider themselves knowledgeable in such matters. But nothing happened, nothing changed, The Wall was still there, and we became even more bored, stagnant and perplexed. Despair, previously unknown to us, set its claws into our very souls—our Reptilian Souls, to be precise.

Thus I, Inanna, Queen of Heaven—I love that title—am returning to speak. I am returning to you, my earthlings, my Lulus. I am returning to prepare you for the coming change in your DNA, for the complete transformation of your planet Earth and your beautiful bodies. And, of course, I hope to liberate myself in the process! I suppose if a mother does not nurture her children properly, she is haunted until she finds a way to balance the scale. It seems I too must balance what I have created, and in some way be a mother to you.

Which brings me to my wonderful childhood on our home planet, Nibiru, and to those who were as mothers to me.

# II

# NIBIRU

In telling my story, I will not bother with linear time as you know it. Earth time is useless to describe our relationship with you. One of our years equals 3,600 Earth years! Pleiadian time is rubbery, expandable, and inter-dimensional. Some of us can travel to any point in time we choose—even alter the events of that time. There is a price to pay for such excursions, but once the talent for them has been mastered, how can one resist? Time travel is fun! Fixed concepts of time simply don't exist, so don't expect them here.

My childhood was a very magical time for me. The cuneiform clay tablets found in Sumer and Babylon say that I was born on Earth, which is true. My twin brother, Utu, came first from my mother's womb, giving him precedence over me in the rights of inheritance. I, however, did not let this unfortunate accident of birth hamper me, and later on in life, I generously compensated myself for this mild frustration.

As soon as we were able to travel, my brother and I were shipped back to our home, Nibiru, an artificial planet which had been designed by Pleiadian technology to seek out raw materials in this solar system, and which orbits through your solar system every 3,600 years. The planet Nibiru was given to our family eons ago, and Anu, my great-grandfather, inherited its rulership from his father before him. Anu is the father of Enlil, and Enlil is father to my father, Nannar. My mother is called Ningal and she is the sweetest lady I have ever known. I love her very much, but I've often wondered how she ever produced me!

My twin brother Utu and I were the first of the royal family to be born on Terra, our name for Earth. At that time, no one knew if Terra's frequencies would affect the DNA of young Pleiadian children. The radiation storms and magnetic fluctuations of this outpost planet were still unpredictable in those days, and our parents and grandparents were taking no chances with our precious genetic codes.

We were brought up in the magnificent palace of my great-grandfather Anu and his sister queen, Antu. My first real memories are of laughing and running across polished lapis lazuli floors; soft breezes gently blew huge white curtains and caressed the beautiful dark curls of my hair. My laughter filled up the house. My little blue body was running for the sheer pleasure of feeling the cool lapis under my chubby little feet! Everyone loved me, and there was no one to control me, only those who would praise and hug me. Life was perfect!

Most of the members of my family have skin of varying blue tones, like the colors of turquoise and a creamy lapis lazuli blended together, warm soft blues that result from the large amounts of copper in our blood. This copper protects us from the cosmic radiation bombarding our planet from space. Our continual tendency to wage war long ago depleted our atmosphere's natural protection against such pernicious radiation, so our bodies adapted by increasing their copper content. We have scattered gold in our stratosphere for eons now to enhance our planet's atmosphere, and we require a constant supply of such gold, which is the primary reason we colonized Terra.

Anu and Antu are the heads of my family and the rulers of Nibiru. Although it is our nature to allow everyone to do exactly as he or she pleases, even to an extreme, most everyone in our quarrelsome bunch will eventually do whatever Anu and Antu say.

*Extreme* is a good word to use to describe Anu and Antu. I know they may seem spoiled, indulgent or excessive, but to me, that was just the way life was, the way we did things. I adored both of my great-grandparents, and they in turn adored me, especially Anu. In fact, my name, Inanna, means "beloved of Anu," and that allowed me some important leverage with the rest of the family later on.

As a child, I was surrounded everywhere by beauty and love. The palace itself was an endless open pavilion with no walls. The architects had designed the indoors to be outdoors and vice-versa, and because we were protected by the frequency regulators, we did not need walls or glass. There were countless paradisiacal gardens of every imaginable design displaying the exotic flowers, plants, birds and butterflies from all corners of the galaxies. Many of the species would be impossible to describe because they are unknown on Terra. Some of the gardens were only frequencies of light and sound; our artists on Nibiru are fond of such creations. The favorite gardens of my great-grandmother, Antu, were made from gold and precious stones, the flowers often being of rubies and sapphires with gold and silver leaves. We re-created these jeweled gardens on Terra to remind us of our home, and in Terra's ancient writings, there are true descriptions of such places.

Anu and Antu were very fond of parties. They celebrated anything, an equinox, a comet, the solstices, and of course, birthdays! The festivities would go on and on, usually for weeks, even months. I assumed everyone lived like this. It was my life.

Anu, handsome and generous, was always thinking of some marvelous gift for his beloved Antu, some new diadem, flying ship, or temple. The palace had to be enormous just to contain the presents he gave her. Antu herself, beautiful and loving, emanated joy and sheer pleasure. Arranging feasts was her passion. Antu had a genius for logistics, and her parties were always organized down to the last napkin ring. She was one of those consummate hostess types who leave you wondering who has the power, the wife or her husband. Everyone from all over the galaxies wanted to be invited to the palace and stuffed with delicacies from Antu's kitchens. Fantastic magical palaces formed from cakes and fruit and ices were temptingly displayed on table after table, and our wines were superb.

Our love of beauty and creativity naturally extends to lovemaking. The act of sexual union is regarded with the highest reverence among my people on Nibiru and throughout the Pleiades. If you bring your earthly concepts of sexuality and morality to my story, you may just as well close the book right now. As we see it, sex is about the frequencies of energy and their direction. Because we use sexual energy to create many things, its focus and amplification is an art form that we all learn and enjoy. We see it as the pure force of energy that emanates from Prime Creator into the body and its receptor centers. Once in the body, it is redirected and transformed according to the ability and capacity of the individual. In some ways it can be likened to an electronic circuitry that modifies and distributes electrical power.

It was Antu and Anu who taught me the knowledge of the Sacred Union. Antu embodies the passionate forces of creation and is considered a great master of such knowledge. I was honored to have her teach me. The power of sexual expression is revered and sought after by us. This knowledge was part of my genetic lineage, and because I am of the blood of Anu and Antu, I was a natural, born to love and to be loved, and thus their favorite.

In the Temples of Love on Nibiru, Anu and Antu chose priests and priestesses for their abilities to receive and transmit the higher frequencies of Sacred Union. We never saw sexual pleasure as anything less than healing and fun. On a larger scale, sexual union is a grand generator of nectar for Prime Creator. The connecting of sex with shame and guilt was perpetrated upon Terra by another member of my family, certainly not by me, in order to enslave the Lulus and keep them in fear. It is common knowledge on Nibiru that sexual power is a natural part of existence.

My childhood on Nibiru was a paradise and I was adored. As I grew older my education was left to my great-aunt Nin. Her real name is Ninhursag, but I call her my Nin because she tenderly cared for me when I was a little girl; she is like a mother to me and I love her dearly. Ninhursag is the daughter of Anu, but not of Antu. Anu could have, and did have, as many mistresses as he chose. We are very allowing and expressive, and it was not considered important that Anu enjoyed many other women. What *was* important to us was the line of succession—who would inherit power from Anu. Sibling marriages are common among us, in order to assure the first line of succession, and Antu was Anu's sister as well as his wife.

I know, you're shocked. But I warned you not to bring your morality to my family matters. On the one hand, marrying your sister made it perfectly clear who would take power, and on the other hand, it made a mess. Anu was passionate and had many children by many women. But all these siblings created great rivalries and confusion in our world, and later on Terra.

Enlil, Enki, and Ninhursag are the three principal children of my great-grandfather, Anu. Enlil and Enki, both male, have different mothers, and Ninhursag, born of yet another mother, is the only female.

Anu and Antu always indulged me, but my great-aunt Nin, by nature disciplined and rigorous, saw that I had a small tendency to let my various impulses get a little out of hand. I naturally never saw this as a problem. Nin was given the thankless task of educating me, and although she was occasionally hard on me, I always knew she loved me deeply. There were many times I depended upon that love.

# III

# NINHURSAG

Ninhursag is also known as the Mother Goddess, the Lady of Life, the Lady of the Mountain, and countless other names of loving affection. A brilliant geneticist and doctor, my great-aunt Nin is the Master Geneticist of the House of Anu. Nin's mother was a beautiful surgeon whom Anu had fallen in love with on a trip to the Planet of Healing. Nin's mother was very different in character from Antu, and as Nin grew up she embodied her mother's impeccable self-discipline and will. Not at all fond of Antu's endless parties, Ninhursag put her passions into the arts of healing and genetic enhancements. She possessed a clear, razor-like mind and the heart of an angel.

Although my Nin grew up on Nibiru, she accompanied her brothers to Terra to aid in its colonization. Enki and Enlil, the two sons of Anu, had been assigned to bring gold and other useful minerals back to Nibiru. Gold was essential to us because of the imbalances in our atmosphere brought about by our incessant warring. Terra in those days was seen solely as a source of minerals, a mining outpost at the edge of the galaxy. Its inhabitants were the wild creatures who roamed her vast plains grazing on an abundance of grasses, and the races of the Snake People and Dragon People who preferred to live in vast tunnels under Terra's crust to protect themselves from the frequent radiation storms and magnetic shifts.

Ninhursag, Enki, and Enlil all went to Terra with a sense of excitement and purpose. Because Enlil was the son of Anu and Antu and the first in line to inherit Anu's power, he was chosen as leader of two groups of Nibiru Astronauts. One group, assigned to the satellite ship, remained in orbit to monitor the planet, to report any difficulties that might arise from space, and to receive the transit shuttles. For the purpose of eventually colonizing the entire planet, the other group, the majority of our Astronauts, went down to Terra to live and work, and these were called the Anunnaki.

Enki, the child of Anu and a Dragon princess of Terra, was second to Enlil in the line of power from his father. Enki was our Master Engineer and had begun the mining projects some time before Enlil's arrival. My family invented sibling rivalry, and as you can well imagine, these two brothers with the same father and different mothers constantly argued over every decision to be made. Ninhursag was our Chief Physician and Master Geneticist on Terra, and by necessity, the family peacemaker.

The Anunnaki, our Astronauts, who quite happily followed these three children of Anu down to Terra, were all truly excited in the early stages of this grand adventure. Promised riches and land, the Anunnaki were content for awhile, but no one was prepared for all that digging! They had never done anything so physical, so repetitious, and working in the gold mines soon became an ominous chore. Enki even tried making up songs to keep their spirits up. But soon these warriors, scientists and engineers became disgruntled, then angry. And, because Pleiadians have a sort of group mind, their discontent spread like dragon fire. They refused to dig one more ounce.

Enlil and Enki were astounded! Zounds! They could always get their fellow Pleiadians motivated at home. What was to be done? They did not want to be disgraced and look bad in their father Anu's eyes. True to the family's nature, the brothers began to blame each other. Cursing and bickering led to blows, and after a little blood and a few bruises, a solution occurred to them. Many species existed on Terra from which they could extract genetic material to create a race of slave workers. This would solve all their problems and keep the Anunnaki happy. It had been done before on other planets. They announced to crowds of cheering Astronauts that the wondrous Bulls of Anu had solved all! The mighty Enlil and the great Enki had complete control of the situation!

They immediately summoned their sister, Ninhursag. Nin also thought it was a good idea. She had been administering healing herbs to the exhausted workers and she did not enjoy watching the brilliant Anunnaki, especially the women, laboring under such brutal conditions. So she and Enki, who was also trained in genetics, retired to the laboratory and began to experiment. Enlil turned to agriculture, to the re-routing of rivers, and the construction of infrastructure, pyramids and dams. Colonizing a planet the size of Terra was a big project.

When I think of Ninhursag and Enki alone in the laboratory experimenting with the various genetic material they had collected, I recall a time when they had a terrible quarrel. Nin completely lost control of herself and came close to killing Enki. Because he was always plotting ways to get an advantage over his brother Enlil, Enki wanted to have a child by their sister. He knew this child, if it were a male, would be considered a rival to Enlil and to the children of Enlil.

So, Enki approached his sister. No one had ever dared to seduce Nin before. It's not that she wasn't beautiful; my great-aunt was very beautiful and kind. But everyone was intimidated by her brilliance, her precise manner and intense self-discipline. I suppose that Ninhursag had always assumed that one day she would marry one of her brothers. Her father Anu had married his sister, as was our custom. So naturally, Ninhursag thought of marrying either Enlil or Enki. But Enki's mother, Id, had persuaded him to marry into her branch of the family on Terra, the Dragon race, and Enlil married a nurse with whom he had fallen passionately in love. So, there wasn't anyone left on this remote planet whom Ninhursag could consider to be her equal. Being pristinely idealistic and headstrong, Nin preferred no one to any she deemed beneath her.

Nin was very innocent about men and not skilled in the arts of seduction, and she was not anticipating that her married brother would court her and indeed show her such lavish ardor and passion. Enki's polished techniques of pursuit went straight to her head. She was blushing like a schoolgirl. Poor Nin simply wasn't used to being flattered and set up by a professional like Enki who had seduced so many other women that he didn't have to think twice about his next move. Ninhursag fell for it hook, line, and sinker. I think it was the first time her feminine ego had been massaged and she was smitten by powerful hormones.

But, much to Enki's disappointment, a girl child was produced by the mating. Ninhursag was delighted and lovingly doted on the child. My Nin never met a baby she didn't love; she revered all of life. Enki waited in a noticeable absence until the girl reached sexual maturity, and to the shock and amazement of Nin, proceeded to seduce this daughter and also impregnate her! Once again, a female was produced, but this did not stop Enki. As soon as the second female child began to ovulate, Enki made advances toward her, determined to produce a male heir.

Ninhursag was outraged! She was sickened by the thought that Enki, their father, could defile and prey upon his own naive little girls, and her pride was deeply wounded. Feeling utterly used, Ninhursag angrily determined to put an end to her brother's despicable folly. She brewed an irresistibly delicious and intoxicating elixir full of deadly, virulent herbs she herself had formulated. As Enki happily drank the liquid, Nin whispered the sacred words of her spell and thus inflicted a powerful curse upon her brother. Enki fell to the ground, cup in hand.

Ninhursag coldly and dispassionately watched as the agonizing effects of a long, slow, painful death swept over him. She wanted him to suffer as he had made her and her daughter suffer; she wanted him to understand pain. The miserable Enki began to shrivel up and age rapidly, his skin turning a putrid yellow. Fearing the worst, Anu, the father of both Ninhursag and Enki, was finally forced to plead with Nin to convince her to relinquish her curse and invoke the healing magic. In time, Enki recovered and begged his sister's forgiveness. But my Nin was changed thereafter and she never again allowed herself to trust in men.

If it seems that my family resembles one of those epic soap operas so popular on Terra, you might ask yourself why.

✳

In the actual creation of the slave laborers, many mistakes were made, some comical, some horrible, some unspeakable. When at last the proper combination of DNA was found and the first Lulu, the perfect worker, was produced, he was made intelligent enough to take orders, but not smart enough to think for himself or to rebel. And he had to be able to hold a shovel!

Among the many species existing on Earth at that time was a creature you call *Homo erectus*. Roaming the steppes with gazelles and other animal friends, members of this genus ate the grasses and vegetation. They possessed the ability to communicate telepathically with the animals and each other. Wild and free, they were at one with the natural wisdom of Terra's frequencies. They were known to us for dismantling the traps we set to capture their animal friends. This human creature and the animals respectfully loved one another. Of all the DNA available to us, that of *Homo erectus* served us best.

Enki volunteered his wife, Ninki, to birth the first Lulu. The genetic material of *Homo erectus* was implanted in the egg of the Pleiadian female. The blood of man was mixed with our blood, the blood of the "gods," and the genetic potentials were fused. Thus the human species carries Pleiadean genetic codes and our DNA is forever combined with yours.

The ovum of the female Anunnaki were used to birth

more Lulus until they were endowed with the ability to reproduce themselves. Not everyone in the family wanted the Lulus to be able to reproduce without our help, but it was far easier to let them carry on the process without us. The human species as you know it was created through the successful genetic manipulations of Ninhursag and Enki to provide us with slave labor in our gold mines. Those first Lulus, your ancestors, saw us as creators, as "gods"; and we encouraged such beliefs, because it made it easier for us to control them.

This is where I came in. A steady stream of fresh laborers was required for their projects by the members of my family and the Anunnaki. As Anu and Antu had instructed me in the arts of love and reproduction, it became my job to educate the Astronauts and the Lulus in the most efficient frequencies of sexual experience. I was delighted! To this purpose, I had fabulous temples constructed and I created wonderful ceremonies and rituals. I wanted my great-grand-mother, Antu, to be proud of me. I modified traditional Pleiadian tantric rituals to suit our purposes on Terra.

We had fun in those days! Some might call my ceremonies orgies, but I personally would never refer to my artistic creations in such a crass manner. The word *orgy* reflects the sad attitude of the present-day culture on Terra toward the most sacred link with Prime Creator. The sexual experience is much more than friction; it is a key to your power, the secretion of all the hormonal systems lifting the energies, merging two beings in Sacred Union. Reverence for the experience produces healthier babies and attracts a soul similar to the frequency which is generated and emitted.

The Lulus' telepathic abilities made them naturals. Those early times were grand indeed; we taught them to never question anything.

# IV

# ENLIL

Enlil is the firstborn of Anu and Antu, the first in line to inherit the power and throne of Anu. Enlil is definitely the son of my great-grandmother, Antu, for he is a real detail person who excels at logistics. From Anu, Enlil inherited his passionate nature, a love of order, and great masculine beauty. Enlil's hair is like gold and falls in the most perfect waves. He is tall in stature even for us, and we are from eight to ten feet tall. His physical prowess is mirrored by a severity and a strict adherence to his own integrity. Enlil is the father of my father, Nannar.

In his entire history, it appears that my grandfather, Enlil, made only one mistake. He raped my grandmother. Everyone in my family has very strong sexual proclivities. When Enlil was still young and full of oats, he took a stroll by the side of a river and came upon a beautiful woman who was swimming naked. Her hair was flowing wet in streams of gold, her body glistening in the sunlight. When he saw her full breasts beneath the waters, lust overcame him.

Poor Enlil had fallen into a trap. The mother of this lovely swimmer had convinced her daughter to seduce Enlil in this manner so that she might make a great marriage, and the plan worked perfectly. Enlil forced himself upon her. This is against our laws. Enlil was found out and arrested. Brought before a council of his peers, Enlil was placed into exile. I don't believe the humiliation of that punishment ever left him. He was in love with the girl and pleaded with her parents to give her in marriage. After their wedding, he was pardoned, but he never forgot and, to my knowledge, he never made another mistake.

Perhaps it was this experience of unbridled passion that left Enlil with a tendency to judge the passions of others. As the Lulus multiplied, the Anunnaki and the members of my family began to copulate with them. The level of sexual interest had gotten a little out of hand and this made Enlil angry. He never thought they should be given the capacity to reproduce without our absolute control. The unique characteristics of the Lulus' telepathic abilities added an unknown thrill to the sexual experience, especially after I had trained them.

The word got around. The "gods" were running off into the woods, frolicking and reproducing with the Lulus. Occasionally, the Anunnaki would throw caution to the wind, abandon their good sense and express their wild passions right there in the streets of Sumer! The little Lulus were so cute! I thought it was fun.

In those times, birth was not the painful process that you know today. Birth was easy and a magical time to be at one with the Goddess of all life. It was a time to experience Union with the Cosmos, to bring forth more expressions of Prime Creator. Not of pain! We were certainly not ashamed of our bodies or their functions. The Nibiruans and the Lulus enjoyed being pregnant. Every birth gave us more Lulus and more festivals, more fun and more beer! Did I mention that with the grains that grew wild upon Terra we developed the most delicious beers, ales, and mead? We gave it to the Lulus as a reward for their work, and we drank it ourselves.

Enlil became more and more disturbed by the wanton copulation of the Anunnaki with the Lulus. He became obsessed, afraid that our genetic lineages were being corrupted by such uncontrolled crossbreeding, and he was angry at the proliferation of Lulus. Unable to sleep, Enlil began to think of ways to cut down on the Lulu population, and after all my hard work.

By this time there were many social hierarchies among the Lulus. There was great discussion as to who had the most "god blood," who was related to which "god," and how long their lineage was—just as some humans today pretend to be related to such-and-such royalty.

We have been on and around Terra now for almost half a million of your years. The Lulus only began to write about us on all those clay tablets around 5,000 years ago. Think of it—centuries elapsed while stories were passed from memory to memory. In earlier times the Lulus had a greater ability to memorize data; however, their perceptions of us as all-knowing "gods" were only whatever we wanted them to be. They were bred *not to question* and those who did were shunned or killed. We required laborers and did not want the Lulus to become our equals; we kept them limited. The clay tablets record only that which we allowed the scribes to write down.

Enlil became more distraught at the thought of the Lulu population over-running Terra. He wanted to get rid of them, but how? And who was to be killed?

Enlil called a meeting of the family. He demanded that something be done about the Lulus and began to pontificate his solemn views on the matter. Naturally, the old rivalry of brother against brother began to heat up. Enki completely disagreed! Enki complained that after all the work he and Ninhursag had done to create such efficient workers, it was absurd to even consider destroying them. Perhaps it had become a bit noisy out there, but at least there were now plenty of hands to dig in the gold mines. The brothers ranted and raved as usual.

Enlil's wrath was immutable, despite his brother's pleas. The sons of Enlil and Enki joined in the arguing, both sides raging for a time. But in the end, because he is the number-one son, Enlil prevailed. His plan would not kill them all, just those unfortunate enough to starve to death, and so the first famine was arranged. As Enki and his sons left the meeting, they must have been formulating a plan to thwart Enlil, for even though the ensuing famine caused cannibalism to spread across the land, some food was smuggled to the Lulus and most survived.

Enlil is supposed to have final authority over the rest of us by his birth, but it just isn't that easy. We are a family of strong-willed individuals. All of us are headstrong about expanding our powers, and we have no real feeling for

38

boundaries or limitations of any sort. Enlil is the same. He is the son of Anu, who never followed anyone but himself in any matter. Once Enlil had made up his mind and set his course, it was not likely we could dissuade him and he did not give up.

Enlil commanded the communications from the space station orbiting Terra, and he was the first to learn of the coming polar shift. High above the planet, the orbiting Astronauts began to observe magnetic fluctuations and the inevitable wobblings. The axis of the planet was about to reverse itself. We had observed this before, but there had never been such a large population to evacuate. Enlil kept these observations secret. He determined to wait until the last possible moment so there would be only enough time to transfer the families of Anu and the Anunnaki to the orbiting station. He made certain there could not be sufficient time to rescue the Lulus. Enlil would have his way over Enki, no matter the cost.

The Great Flood came upon us all unexpectedly. Enki sent his pilot, Matali, to take me above. I had not even packed! I recall standing in my dressing rooms trying to decide what jewelry to take. I had so much, lovely gold and lapis lazuli necklaces, bracelets of emerald and ivory; if I could only take a few more trunks on the shuttle. Matali was laughing at my frustration and advising me to hurry. I did not yet understand the severity of what was coming.

I remember so vividly sitting in the shuttle, crying in Ninhursag's arms. From the portals we could see wave after wave engulfing the plains of Terra and sweeping our precious Lulus into the deep. I had never before experienced loss, and I was not prepared to feel such grief. It was as if I, too, were drowning. In my heart I could hear the cries of the desperate Lulus. In the Eye of my Mind, I saw the women I had trained in my Temples as priestesses clinging to the columns, praying to me, of all things. But their prayers went unanswered as the waters submerged them in death, their white gowns floating for a brief moment in billowy puffs...and then all was gone.

My heart broke. I had not known how much I loved the Lulus. I had not known a part of me would remain with them underneath that cruel deluge. Only Ninhursag seemed to share my sorrow. We wept in despair. And who would make us lovely ales to drink? Who would mine the gold?

For once the rivalry between Enlil and Enki proved useful. The spies of Enki had informed him of the polar shift. In all the ancient cultures of Terra there are tales of a flood and one man who was saved in an ark. Enki chose that man. Knowing there would be a great flood, Enki resolved to save at least one family of Lulus. In his vanity, he picked a man from his own gene pool. All those stories about Noah being chosen for his goodness, well, Noah even *looked* like Enki. And there was no ark as you know it. It was a submarine, and the animals "two-by-two" were actually genetic material appropriately stored so they might later be re-created. Defying Enlil, Enki rescued the Lulus.

Upon discovering the surviving Lulus, Enlil was furious. He and his sons hurled accusations of treason and other heinous crimes against Enki and his sons. Enlil claimed that Enki had defied the laws of Anu. Thereupon Enki made the greatest speech of his life, cleverly praising and flattering Enlil for his "divine" plan. In the greatness of his visionary wisdom, Enlil had been fated to engineer a method of sorting through the rubbish of the species to arrive at the prime genetic material of all the Lulus. And if these lone survivors were deemed to live through the horrors of the Deluge, their genes must be worthy of serving Anu and the Nibiruans.

To our amazement, Enlil went for it! He must have been having second thoughts, wondering where he was going to get the workers he needed to mine the gold and build all his monuments.

Each member of the family then swore a vow to never again destroy the Lulus. In a burst of heartfelt generosity and maybe a little guilt, Enlil granted Noah eternal life, at least as we know it. All manner of laws were subsequently made to regulate the copulation and breeding of the Lulus. Even though it had turned out all right in some ways, there was a shift, a further parting and enmity between Enlil and Enki. Many of us knew there was more to come from the great rivalry.

V

# ENKI

We Pleiadians consider ourselves to be of the Reptilian racial base. As evidence of our connection to you, the human species possesses a reptilian brain located in the cerebellum which controls the autonomic functions of the body. In all the worlds, including the Pleiadian star system, many races abound. There are no words in your language to describe these races. You could not even pronounce their names, because the sounds would be foreign to you.

When Anu first came to Terra 500,000 years ago, the Dragon People and the Snake People were already here. Naturally, they were reluctant to share their planet. Anu wanted the gold, but the Dragon People feared Anu would not respect their peaceful ways. They had spent eons setting lines of magnetic energy around Terra and had constructed endless tunnels in cooperation with the Snake People. The energy vortexes which power their civilizations are in these tunnels, along with enormous stores of precious stones and metals. Quite a few battles ensued on Terra and in her skies. Finally, arrangements were made, territories were drawn, and Anu agreed to mate with a Dragon princess named Id to seal the alliance. From this coupling came the male child Enki.

Id is superbly beautiful. Anu found her greenish golden metallic skin and deep red eyes mysteriously appealing. Their son, Enki, has an air of aristocratic elegance, and he has a tail. I like the tail. I think it adds mystery to his Merlin-like face. He also has pointed ears with long lobes, which seems to have caused some confusion about who he is, but Enki's resemblance to the mythical creature called the Devil is purely accidental. My dear Enki is a softhearted sort whose main flaw lies in an inability to say no to anyone. He is most assuredly not a devil.

Enki was educated on Nibiru. His mother, Id, did not care for the never-ending parties given by my great-grandmother, Antu, so Enki and Id were happy to move to Terra. There Id lived with her people in the tunnels, and Enki built himself a beautiful kingdom in the sea called the Abzu. The structures of the Abzu were built of silver and lapis lazuli, part high on a mountain, and part submerged under water. This was very practical as the submerged part offered protection from the unpredictable waves of radiation that swept across Terra in those early days.

When Enki wasn't working in the Abzu, he built dams and rerouted waters. Loving water, he frequently paddled around the marshes of Sumer and Babylon in a little boat all by himself, studying fish, insects, and the grasses along the river banks. Enki loved this planet. I suppose he got that from Id; the beauty of Terra flows in the blood of her ancient people.

Unfortunately, Anu sent Enlil to Terra after Enki had already been there for awhile. When Enlil arrived to take command of the colony, he made a big deal about his being the true son of Anu and left Enki with little choice. Domains were divided. Enki was to keep the Abzu and Egypt. Enlil took the rulership of Sumer, the mining operations in Africa, the Spaceport, and command of the Astronauts, both those orbiting around and living on Terra. Ninhursag told me that even as children Enlil and Enki had fought. She secretly thought that it was Antu's idea to ship them all off to Terra so their endless arguing wouldn't interfere with her parties.

Enki didn't exactly encourage the Dragon People to cooperate with his half-brother, Enlil. The Dragons naturally preferred Enki as he was one of them, and he was very protective of his mother, Id. Whatever decisions Enlil made, Enki disagreed with. This wreaked havoc upon Terra. Neither son was right or wrong, each wanted his own way. They both wanted complete control. The sons of Enki and Enlil came to share the same animosities, and their fathers did not hesitate to use them in their conflicts. The entire family and the Lulus were dragged into this rivalry, which has been the catalyst for all of Terra's unfortunate history.

Even though I am the granddaughter of Enlil, I always enjoy the company of Enki. Enki is someone you can have fun with. Enki loves women, all of them! Enlil is so serious. Enki and Enlil are oil and water.

As time on Terra passed, the territories kept being subdivided among the sons of Enki and the sons of Enlil to prevent war. It was easy to see that if I didn't take matters into my own hands, I would wind up with nothing in this contentious group, so I decided to pay Enki a visit.

I dressed in my finest gown and jewels, and flew down to the Abzu. I knew that Enki kept the *Divine MEs* in the Abzu and I was hoping to take advantage of his weakness for women and drink. The *MEs* are based on a technology that is only now being discovered on Terra. Imagine a computer with all the knowledge in the Universe. This computer transfers knowledge into the mind of the user in the form of a hologram. Thus knowledge is transferred to the user holographically as a totality, so learning does not take place bit by bit in a linear manner. The possessor of the *MEs* has complete understanding of the information in each *ME* instantly. Knowledge is power—power to create civilizations, to predict the movement of the stars, to travel beyond Terra, to regulate the atmosphere, all the sciences and arts. I wanted this power for myself.

As always, Enki was delighted to see me. Praising my beauty and charms, he hugged me inappropriately. Enki's servants followed us into a cozy den with trays of delicious delicacies imported from Nibiru, exquisitely prepared cakes and Sumerian beers. When Enki was distracted, I doused his beer with my own magical herbs. These herbs enhance one's frequency, especially elderly gentlemen whose potencies might be fading. Enki was having a wonderful time and he couldn't take his eyes off me, alluring as I am. Enki was soon putting back goblets of beer, one after the other. Enki has a wonderful sense of humor and I was telling him the most amusing stories about the priestesses in my temples. We feasted, drank, and laughed for three days. More than once I danced for Enki, something like the seven-veil number which can be so effective. He loved that!

At last, I asked him for the *MEs*. Many of the sons already possessed them, and I only wanted my own set. At first he was reluctant; he knew it was forbidden. It would make Enlil furious if I got them without his permission. Enlil would have to be told. So, I poured Enki another drink. I didn't see why the great Enki should have to ask his brother Enlil for anything! I told him a particularly juicy temple story. While he was still laughing, I begged him for the *MEs* in my sweetest voice. Enki was so thrilled by my enticements, he finally said yes! I think he also was enjoying the thought of how much it would aggravate Enlil.

Enki was feeling the effects of the herbs and began to fall into a nap. As he started to snore, I gathered the *MEs* into a golden case I had brought along. The *MEs* appear as twelve-sided crystals of great beauty and color and can be activated only if you know the sacred sounds that make them vibrate and emit their secrets. Ninhursag had taught me these sounds on Nibiru.

As Enki's snoring grew louder, I slipped out the door with the *MEs*. I had brought two spacecraft with me. One was official, and the other was my private ship. I had a feeling Enki might change his mind and try to get the *MEs* back when he woke up. So I sent my official ship home as a decoy and flew away in my small ship, which I am quite capable of piloting, alone with the *MEs*.

When Enki woke from his nap, he didn't quite remember everything and his servants had to remind him that he had given the *MEs* to his beloved Inanna. Feeling a little used and abandoned, Enki's male ego flew into gear. He loudly ordered his servants to chase me down, to bring me and the *MEs* back to him. I knew it was a pretense to get me back, and to pacify Enlil and the other gods. I had cleverly foreseen this possibility and was hidden safely underground in a Dragon sanctuary with my *MEs*.

It is the way of the family of Anu, that if you have the will to take power, you are respected for it. Enki and Enlil were so impressed by my daring, they granted me the right to keep the *MEs*. They made me a member of the family council, the Pantheon of Twelve. I had gotten all I had wanted and more! I declared myself the Queen of Heaven and Earth. I now possessed the technology to start my own cities and I acquired a more powerful place within my family. I obtained power because I had courageously seized it, and I'm still very fond of Enki!

# VI

# DUMUZI

Even though it may seem that I led a charmed life and was totally spoiled, things began to look pretty grim for me. In order to take my rightful place in the family of Anu, I had to marry someone whose genetic lineage would give me power. I had grown up competing with my brother, Utu, and the other young males, and I thought of myself as their equal. The idea of getting married and being dominated by anyone in this gene pool wasn't too thrilling for me.

In Pleiadian culture, the feminine energy was revered, and the law allowed equal rights for women, as well as the opportunity to express their inborn talents. However, the majority of women relied heavily on a "good marriage" to define their place in the world. You might say that Pleiadian females were considered equal to their men, but with conditions, and the perimeters of those conditions were drawn by the individual nature of each woman.

My brother, Utu, and of course, my parents were constantly after me to make a powerful marriage which would make our branch of the family all the more impressive. Utu would taunt me by asking if I wanted to end up like Ninhursag. I had seen the life of my great-aunt Nin as an old-maid spinster, and I didn't like the looks of it. Secure in the power they received through marriage, most of the women of my family quietly took their places at their husbands' sides. *Quietly* was a word I didn't much care for. I wanted power for myself; I didn't want to be controlled by anyone!

Nevertheless, with all this pressure on me to get married, I began to look around and ask myself who was available that I found interesting.

Enlil had succeeded in bearing a son by Ninhursag; another defeat over Enki, who had produced only daughters with her. The boy's name was Ninurta, and he was educated with Utu and me on Nibiru. I had already spent too much time with Ninurta as a child and we were always competing with each other, usually quarreling. His mother, Ninhursag, simply doted on him in a disgusting manner; he was so spoiled. Ninurta might be genetically suitable, but he was totally out of the question.

Enki had several sons, but the only one who was available was the youngest, Dumuzi. Ah yes, Dumuzi. Even the name just leaves you flat, doesn't it?

Because Dumuzi was the youngest of Enki's sons, he had the lowliest job; he was assigned the Office of Royal Shepherd. I wonder who made that title up! Okay, so he was in charge of all the domestic animals on Terra. I know, we all have to eat, and the flocks are very important to the survival of the Lulus. I've heard all these arguments from my brother,

49

Utu, and my parents. But have you ever cozied up to the smell of sheep at the end of the day? My parents favored the match. I guess they couldn't wait to get me married off and out of trouble.

I consoled myself with the thought of being part of Enki's family. I could usually get Enki to do something fun with me, and I had plans to become the queen of Egypt. I saw myself floating down the Nile on a golden barge, reclining upon a bed of flowers, the crowds cheering. With the MEs in my possession and a powerful marriage, my budding ambitions were beginning to take shape. So I married Dumuzi.

Marriage was, well, marriage. Dumuzi just wasn't very bright, and he was certainly no match for me. I think his older brothers had brutalized him considerably, especially Marduk, the eldest. Dumuzi was vain and selfish. He actually sat around gazing at himself in a mirror expecting me to wait on him hand and foot! His mother lived for him, granting his every whim. I began to avoid Dumuzi as much as possible.

I was so bored, I took on extra duties at the Temples of Love, as my temples came to be named. I would make all manner of excuses and fly my ship from temple to temple inaugurating all sorts of new ceremonies. I was behaving exactly like modern-day executives who go on business trips to get away from their wives. I created a host of new rituals that centered around Dumuzi and me as a gesture to pacify Dumuzi and our families. The rituals contained all this elaborate stuff about our marriage and lovemaking, about the shy bride and her wonderful husband. This first soap opera gave the Lulus ideals to model their own lives on. The rituals were designed to inspire them to produce children in a happy environment. For me, it was an escape to fantasy fiction. I created my life in ritual the way I wanted it to be, but it wasn't.

Maybe it was my lack of enthusiasm for Dumuzi that left us without a child. To secure our rights to power, there had to be a son to inherit that power; it was the law. But, whatever the reason, we produced no heir. So, I got this idea. If everyone else had produced a child with their sister, why not Dumuzi? Anu and Antu had borne Enlil. Enlil had produced that brat, Ninurta, with Ninhursag. I was inspired.

It was easy to convince Dumuzi to seduce his sister. I raved on about his family's wonderful genetic lineage, and his narcissistic need to reproduce himself did the rest. The sister of Dumuzi was called Geshtinanna, and she was terribly innocent, not at all ambitious like me. I arranged for my servants to prepare an elaborate picnic, complete with herbal wines to stimulate the libido. They were to meet on a beautiful hillside overlooking the flocks that were doing what all animals do in the spring. I had thought of everything, and Geshtinanna, naive as she was, didn't have a clue that she was being set up. After a glass of wine or two, Dumuzi got to the part about them having a child together and the fun went right out of the picnic. Geshtinanna protested; she had this idea about remaining pure for her husband, whoever that might be. Dumuzi tried to persuade her, but she outright refused. Dumuzi lost control and raped her! I suppose it was those herbs I put in the wine, which are so effective on men.

Rape! It was the one thing Dumuzi could not get away with. Not even Enlil had gone unpunished for this crime. Dumuzi and I had now given his elder brother, Marduk, a perfect reason to get rid of his little brother. Marduk had been systematically working to take control of Egypt for himself. Marduk doesn't like me, and he wasn't taking any chances with my ambitions or the dynasties I was hoping to create.

Dumuzi ran to his mother and me, plagued with nightmares and forebodings of his death. We encouraged him to flee and made plans to meet him in secret with food and water. He could hide out until things blew over, until I could talk to Anu and plead his case. But Marduk lost no time. His henchmen pursued Dumuzi into the hills and trapped him like a little rabbit. It was awful. Perhaps Marduk's men got carried away. Whatever actually happened that day, poor Dumuzi died from the radiation weapons heartlessly aimed at him. My husband was dead, and I was still childless.

That was the moment I remembered a useful Pleiadian law: if a man died without an heir, yet had a brother, that brother, whether he was already married or not, was bound to marry the widow and produce a child with her. Luckily Dumuzi had such a brother, Nergal, so handsome and intelligent; I had always admired him. How unfortunate that he was already married to my half-sister in the UnderWorld. Oh, well, I never let little complications stand in my way. I decided to pay a visit to the blond bombshell herself, the Queen of the Dark UnderWorld, Ereshkigal, to claim my rightful husband, *her* husband, Nergal.

# VII

# ERESHKIGAL

Ereshkigal is my half-sister. With a wife as sweet and beautiful as my mother, one might hope my father, Nannar, would have been content. But, marital fidelity was not the way of the family of Anu. Maybe it was the contrast to my mother that made Ereshkigal's mother so fascinating. The only word that even comes close to describing her species is *Raksasas*. She was half-snake and half-demon, totally sexy, sort of oozing and writhing in Kundalini. Her skin was of a coppery light green, her hair was what you might call dreadlocks, and her body was strong and voluptuous. Her eyes were the eyes of a cobra, with the power to hypnotize Nannar. As the Moon God, my father certainly had his dark side.

The passionate attraction between these two could only be described as spontaneous combustion. Ereshkigal was a true child of erotic fusion. No one ever questioned

Ereshkigal's stunning beauty; she was the best of both her parents, and she knew it.

I can't blame her for never liking me. I suppose in a way she felt the same way about me as Enki felt about Enlil. I was the true daughter of Nannar, and she was the concubine's offspring. Enki felt a sympathetic bond with Ereshkigal, besides being enthralled with her beauty. He and my half-sister even conceived a son together whose name was Ningishzidda. Enki, as usual, just couldn't control himself, and as the Chief Mining Engineer, he had given Ereshkigal the domain of the UnderWorld. Enki is a soft touch and I would have enjoyed watching Ereshkigal work her considerable charms on him; we girls do what we can in this world to get by. But, as for all that blond hair, it's as fake as all those hairpieces she adds to give her the big-hair look!

The UnderWorld isn't exactly *under*, although some of it is. It is located in what you now call Africa, and the vast deposits of gold we covet are there. It was an extensive mining operation. Shuttles constantly flew from Terra to the orbiting station delivering refined ores. From deep within the Earth, we took gold and other precious commodities such as silver, copper, uranium, and diamonds. There had to be an immense work force and over the centuries, men and women were bred to become more efficient laborers. Our geneticists were constantly improving on their obedience and docility; however, discipline occasionally became necessary.

On Terra there were at least three species that ate human flesh and the Flesh Eaters were a very useful disciplinary tool. What could scare a recalcitrant worker better than the thought of being eaten alive?

Think of it from our point of view: we were doing our duty. We had to supply the home planet, Nibiru, with gold particles for the depleted atmosphere or we would all die. We did whatever it took to get the gold out of the mines. Ereshkigal was perfect for this job; it didn't faze her at all to motivate the workers with stories of cannibalism. She had just a little bit of that Flesh Eater tendency in her. Not that she ate humans all the time, just an occasional bite.

Cannibalism has different meanings for different species. One group might see it as a way of absorbing the strength, wisdom, and power of the person being eaten. For them, it is a ritualized means of expanding their consciousness as well as physical and sexual prowess. In consuming their enemy, they gain his life's experience. Others only eat the brain of their victim to gain his intelligence. There are remnants of this on your planet today.

A more prevalent type of cannibalism is far more subtle. There are those who know the arts of devouring people's energy without them even knowing it. Think how fear can make you ill, how drained and exhausted one feels from anger, rage, or jealousy. Where does that energy go? Why do those who are addicted to alcohol or drugs appear so tired and pale? Perhaps your controllers no longer need to eat your flesh.

Now you know where all those stories come from about people being taken to the UnderWorld, roasted and eaten by devils! For some it was a reality. But there are no devils, only various species who have controlled you through fear.

This is a free-will Universe, which means that you are free to do whatever you want to do, and so is everyone else. There is *the* problem. If we all start as equals, how do we convince others to do what we want them to do? Are there any rules? Can you trick others? Who values whom and what? If you become a tyrant to another, does that tyranny come back to you? Does it eventually block you? This is the question most interesting to us now, now that we are stuck with *The Wall*.

I certainly wasn't contemplating any metaphysical questions as I flew my ship down to the UnderWorld. My brother, Utu, and my mother and father said that I must not have a brain in my head. They didn't seem to think that Ereshkigal would welcome her newly widowed half-sister with open arms, and they all warned me not to go. But, I had other things on my mind, like her husband Nergal's gene pool and his big blue eyes. By rights, he would become my husband too, and we would produce heirs.

Ereshkigal was rumored to have a fabulous palace, everything covered in gold. I suppose she needed the glitz to cheer her up. Living so far away from Sumer and Egypt must have been depressing for her.

As I approached the gates, I was a little overwhelmed with the gold and marble columns depicting writhing snake monsters devouring terror-stricken Lulus. A bit much, I thought. That was only the beginning.

I had the good sense to send my servant, Ninshubar, back to my ship to wait for me. I told her that if I didn't show up in three days she should fly home and get help. I had listened somewhat to Utu and my parents. Still, I was confident; a girl has to take chances, to have courage. After all, I had dared to acquire the *Divine MEs* from Enki; I could be very persuasive. Ereshkigal didn't exactly come running out of her palace to greet me. In fact, she was nowhere to be seen. I was met by this gruesome gatekeeper who said his name was Neti. God, he or it was big!

I told this overgrown monster who I was, and he began to lead me through a maze with a series of gates which must have been a security system rigged up to protect all of Ereshkigal's gold. Then this gatekeeper ordered me, Inanna, to remove my protective jewels and garments. We all wore a variety of shielding devices to protect us from radiation, and I was also equipped with the usual headgear with field regulators and communication systems. My gown had the standard protective shielding woven into the fabric. You never knew what you might run into flying in space, or on Terra for that matter.

By the time we arrived at the seventh gate, I was ordered to remove my dress. Not that I was modest, but I was becoming a little annoyed at the way I was being treated. Plus, I wanted to know where all my jewelry was being taken. Finally, I entered a room where Ereshkigal was holding court.

It was just as everyone had said; there was a huge ' golden dais with Ereshkigal seated on a majestic throne encrusted with diamonds. I was getting ready to be pleasant, however naked, when these ogre-like judges rose and began to hurl accusations of treachery and treason at me. It was ridiculous. I couldn't imagine what they were talking about, and I was thirsty.

Suddenly, Ereshkigal pulled out this plasma gun and in a Pleiadian minute zapped me with a heavy dose of radiation, more than enough to kill me. I was astounded!

I soon found myself floating above my precious little body, which was rapidly turning from its natural shade of warm blue to a dead indigo!

Ereshkigal ordered her guards to hang my beautiful body on the wall as in a butcher shop. Gag! I lost no time watching my corpse rot. Astral traveling, I followed my servant, Ninshubar, back to Nippur, the city of my grandfather, Enlil. I watched as she went to his temple and begged Enlil to save me. He refused! He said I should have known better than to go down there in the first place; it was common knowledge that Ereshkigal had no love for me.

So my servant went to my father, Nannar. He also said no! I just floated there in the air, listening to my father lecturing on how headstrong I was and how everyone knew I was headed for trouble when I went down there chasing after Ereshkigal's husband. He even went so far as to say I probably got just what I deserved! My own father! Maybe he had wanted another boy?

I was still hovering in space, trying to get used to not having a body. I placed a thought form in the mind of my beloved servant and she quickly moved to Enki's Abzu. By this time, she had worked up a very appealing sob story and, bless old Enki's heart, he decided to intervene. He had some clout with Ereshkigal; it was he who had given her the UnderWorld. He made arrangements to have my body flown to the Great Pyramid, and with the help of my great-aunt Ninhursag, brought me back to life.

I had a terrible headache for three days. I resolved never to visit that witch again and to forget all about her husband's DNA.

Being outside my body wasn't so bad, but it started me thinking how much I enjoyed certain things, like dancing, or even eating. I had become attached to being me and to my life on Terra with the Lulus. The time I spent out of my body made me love Terra all the more. I also learned not to rely too heavily on anyone but myself.

I decided to expand my Love Temples in the eastern territories where I had been given lands that no one else wanted. On the banks of the Indus River, I built the cities Mohenjo-Daro and Harappa.

# VIII

# THE TEMPLES OF LOVE

The mouth of the Indus River was the center of trade from the East at this time. I set my mind and the *Divine MEs* to work creating business and trade between Sumer, Babylon, Egypt, and the Indus Valley. I love the treasures of Terra and I have a gift for business. I am a born trader. My temples were offices of exchange which served as places to barter and deal in various commodities, as well as halls of learning and worship.

I invited my mother, Ningal, to help in designing and building my temples. She has a passion for architecture, and she brought along her close friend, Maya, the most famous architect of our time, to plan Mohenjo-Daro and Harappa. Maya had already designed other temples in Sumer, but Ningal, Maya, and I set about to surpass previous creations. The three of us built such remarkable and beautiful structures that Anu and Antu came to marvel at them.

I have always been fond of lapis lazuli; its deep blues accent my skin tones nicely. But there was never enough of it to build entire temples, so I asked Enki to develop a substitute in his laboratories. In a short time, I had as much lapis as I had ever dreamed of, and I covered the floors of the temples, the columns, and roof tiles with this new faux lapis, my gift from Enki. Marble and gold were tastefully blended with turquoise, malachite, and lapis in geometric rhythms.

I also invited Tara to help me in the temples. Tara is the wife of my friend, Matali, Enki's pilot. Matali doesn't think much of my family. I suppose he has known us "gods" too long. He prefers to put his trust in the Snake People and so he married Tara, his beautiful Snake Princess.

Tara's lineage goes back on the planet Terra farther than any other. Matali says the Snake People are far wiser than those of Nibiru! He has told me magical stories of their kingdom deep within the planet. It is said they play with frequencies we do not understand, and the acquisition of material power does not interest them.

What I did understand was that Tara could dance better than anyone I had ever seen. I knew Tara's dancing style would attract merchants from all over the East to my temples, and she would be a great asset, so I invited her to train my temple dancers. Tara is a lovely woman with creamy pale green skin and dark almond eyes that twinkle like stars in the night sky. Strings of black pearls and gold beads cover her firm bare breasts. My friend, Tara, helped me to establish a grand and flourishing culture.

I also invited Ninhursag. It had become Nin's passion to stay up in her pyramid and administer healing to her beloved Lulus. Her love and compassion for all living beings made her our greatest physician. She had a staff of wonderful nurses who assisted her, but I knew she was lonely. She spent far too much time with that son of hers, Ninurta, which wasn't good for either of them. You know the type of mother who gossips endlessly with her son about the rest of the family? Well, that was my Nin.

I wanted Ninhursag to set up what you might call hospitals, but we consider your modern medicine absolutely barbaric. We work with thought forms and frequencies, not drugs and scalpels. Being the only unmarried matriarch on Terra was taking its toll on Nin, and I loved her. She was even aging ever so slightly, though she would never admit to any of this. Nin presented herself as crisp and competent as ever, only *I* knew better. I was feeling a little lonely myself, and saw how bravely she carried on.

Watching Ninhursag's life, coupled with my own experiences, was beginning to give me a feeling for women. As time passed on Terra, the men in my family were becoming more and more dominating. It was as if the very atmosphere of this remote planet was somehow changing us all.

In the Pleiades, women are revered as symbols of the Great Goddess and treated with respect. It is strongly forbidden by Pleiadian law to strike or rape a woman. Earth's frontier frequencies seemed to bring about a shift in this tradition. Our men were developing a new attitude to the female half of the species. The sons of Enki, led by Marduk, created laws forbidding women certain freedoms in their territories. I was naturally angry and upset by these ridiculous laws, so in my lands, I emphasized the empowerment and enhancement of female energy, and I decided to teach the Lulus some of the Pleiadian Mysteries.

When Ninhursag and Enki created the Lulus, they left a few key components inactivated. Although the Lulus and all the humans born of them, including the present-day inhabitants of Terra, possess our genes, some of these genes don't work because some had been purposefully unplugged. The Lulus were taught to call my family "divine," but we were hardly that. The children of Anu are the eternal adolescents, and words like *ambitious* and *greedy* might describe us more accurately. We had intentionally left the genetic codes of our worker race only partially functional so they would be easier to manage. I knew I could not interfere with the workings of the Lulus' DNA, but no one could stop me from teaching them certain secrets. And since thought creates reality, I hoped a few of my priestesses or priests might fire up the "divine genes" present in all the Lulus and thus instigate their latent evolution through hormonal secretion.

In your present time, the Samkhya is all that remains of Pleiadian wisdom. *Samkhya* is a Sanskrit word meaning "to enumerate." The concept of Samkhya suggests that matter is organized out of two primary components, consciousness and energy, which interact to create the universe.

It is conscious focused thought that moves the frequencies of energy to form themselves into the myriad, infinite Play of all the Worlds! Physicists in your present time are approaching this understanding, but they are missing one component, and that is Love. Not the kind of love you have experienced as humans, something limited and unpredictable, but Love as a primary force. It would never occur to a modern-day scientist to quantify a state of consciousness such as Love, but that is the secret. Love is the missing piece in all of the unified field theories.

It is the Love from Prime Creator that is the first cause of this Universe and all other dimensional realities in existence. Do not your great ones say that Love is the greatest of all qualities? Yet, it is too simple, too obvious for most.

So, I taught this Samkhya in my temples. I taught my

girls and some of the men who wanted to learn how to use their beautiful minds and bodies to bring this force, the force of divine Love, onto Terra, into our cities, our fields, and our children.

It was a wonderful time for us all. Business thrived, and the women were allowed to own property and to keep their wealth separate if they so chose. Thus, no one owned them. Both sexes were sovereign unto themselves, and the men were equally happy. There was a flowering of civilization and the arts. Our fields were abundant, trade with Sumer and Egypt was booming, and the arts of dance, song, painting, and sculpting soared to new heights. Reports of Maya's architectural achievements spread around the world.

Of all the rituals we initiated in my temples, the Ritual of Marriage was the favorite. The priestesses would dress and prepare the bride, who was educated in the arts of pleasing her husband and the ways of ensuring conception when it was desired. The husband was also prepared and instructed in these matters. In those times, it was common knowledge that the greatest pleasure was achieved by arousing the female to a height of ecstasy. The bride became the channel for all the feminine energy in creation, and the husband became all male energy. Their union allowed the forces of Prime Creator and the Great Goddess to express on Terra.

The secret of this sort of union is focus. We trained the couple to attain intense concentration by gazing into each other's eyes while they are joined in union. Every cell of the body, every awareness of the being must be in the moment, every thought must be focused on the now. A woman cannot hope to achieve higher states of consciousness in union if she is fretting about the grocery list or some other nonsense. Reflecting on the past or worrying about the future only weakens the experience.

We formulated wines and elixirs to enhance focus for those who required a little help, but our greatest practitioners required no assistance in their grand focus. The energies they generated assured the fertility of our agriculture and the happiness of our people, and often healed the sick.

One aspect of my Indus Valley was the love and veneration of animals. We used elephants and oxen in our trading business, and we became so fond of our animals that we honored them in the temples. I had reserves created for the old ones where they could retire in safety. There they were loved and protected, visited frequently by children. Many of the Lulus still possessed the gift of speaking with animals, and these were sought after to train and manage elephants, water buffalo, oxen, lions, gazelles, animals of all sorts.

To this day, my eyes fill up with tears as I remember my pet lions. These two creatures loved me with all their considerable hearts and were a great blessing to me. The wisdom they taught me will always be with me. The male lion allowed me to ride on his back through the streets and almost never left my side. The female guarded me with the fierce instincts of a mother. Surely, I never experienced greater love and loyalty than that which they gave to me.

After a few hundred of your years, the excitement of being in the Indus Valley and creating a new civilization there began to wear thin for me. Business was great, the temples were built, and my priestesses were so well trained they could easily run things without me. My friend, Matali, was flying me back and forth to the Sumerian city of Uruk to check on grain deliveries and such. I missed being in Sumer; I missed Egypt and Enki's Abzu. My cities were less sophisticated, and I didn't have a spaceport with access to the orbiting station. I felt stuck in the hinterlands.

And I had no husband. Matali said I was lucky not to be married to any of my relatives, being what they were in his estimation!

Bemusing my dilemma, a wonderful idea occurred to me. Back in Uruk, Anu was bestowing the powers of king-ship on some of the more shining Lulus of that time. Anu delegated limited power to those who would rule the cities and city states. We gave the Lulus dominion over those human affairs which held no interest for us.

Kingship was becoming an important new part of life on Terra. Why shouldn't I be the one to bestow this power? If I could talk Anu into letting me take over, he wouldn't have to bother, and he would have more time for himself and for Antu's parties. I knew Antu would like the idea.

Antu had always loved me, and I had put her face on the statues of the goddess in my temples. Being Anu's sister gave her unquestioned power, and she had political connec-tions throughout the galaxies. Her liaisons were textbook classics. Antu never seemed to mind Anu's constant stream of concubines. I always suspected she knew how to place herself into states of ecstatic consciousness. She is such a happy lady, filled with what you call *joie de vivre!*

To convince Anu and Antu that I was right for the job of choosing kings, I built a temple in Uruk. The temple itself was dedicated to Anu. Deep in the interior, in the most important area, I placed a bed of solid gold with Antu's name beautifully and noticeably engraved upon it. The bed was raised on a dais, and magnificently adorned with fresh flowers and flowing silks. This temple in Uruk was called the Dwelling Place of Anu. But the bed enshrined within symbolized to everyone which woman Anu listened to. What a touch! They both loved it! When I asked to be given the Right to Grant Kingship, they agreed. It was understood that Anu would be informed of my decisions. My great-grandmother, Antu, was delighted at the prospect of my new career. And what better way to find a husband?

# IX

# MARDUK AND WAR

Marduk, the eldest son of Enki, is the last man in the galaxy I would ever want for a husband! Enki, who loved life and women of all races, produced many, many children. All of these children competed with each other for lands, kingdoms, armies, and wealth.

My late husband, Dumuzi, who was the youngest of the principal children, was safely dead and no longer a threat to the others. Nergal, married to my half-sister, Ereshkigal, was second in the line to power. Enki even produced a child by his daughter-in-law, Ereshkigal. Perhaps that is how she received the UnderWorld, where Nergal ruled with her. There were countless other children by Enki, a veritable snake pit of bickering brothers and sisters.

And then there was Marduk, who claimed everything for himself. Some might think Marduk was from Mars.

Whatever Marduk's actual genes were, he was born a natural reptilian tyrant! He came right out of his mother's womb calculating how he was going to control everything and everybody. All the classic reptilian traits seem to come together in one big Marduk.

Marduk is very tall, with piercing red eyes and golden-olive skin that is a little on the scaly side. He has the remnants of gills on his cheeks. Originally, he was born with a tail like his father, Enki, but later in his life, he had the tail removed by laser surgery. He claimed the tail merely got in his way, but we all knew it was sheer vanity that drove him. Many find Marduk exquisitely beautiful, coldly magnificent, with a brilliant mind and the focus of a cobra. He does possess a kind of beauty, if you like that sort.

The sons of Enki were always quarreling with each other, even as children. As Enki and his brother, Enlil, fought over power, so did *their* children. There might be temporary alliances, but sooner or later, one would want to have his own way and brothers would come to blows. As children, some of the boys received terrible wounds from those little toy plasma guns. A few of the rivaling mothers taught their children how to place thought forms of imaginary demons into the dreams of the other little ones. The women learned that if their sons held power, so would the mothers, and they began to neglect their daughters, seeking only powerful marriages for the poor things.

A family gathering was usually a chaotic disaster, occasionally achieving the magnitude of a riot. The boys would fight, and their mothers would egg them on. Enki usually retired in fear and despair; he never liked to discipline anyone.

After considerable struggle and deceit, Marduk was given Egypt to rule. Enki really preferred to stay in the Abzu experimenting with his various projects, genetic and otherwise, so he handed over the dominion of the river Nile and its surrounding territories to his lordship, Marduk. Marduk immediately set about building enormous monolithic statues of himself everywhere. These works of art enhanced his beauty and were designed to intimidate, or simply scare the pants off, the Lulus. Rule by intimidation was Marduk's code. All the tyrants in Terra's history have been inspired in one way or another by Enki's firstborn.

Because Egypt was Enki's domain, it was left to his offspring to regulate the weather patterns around the Nile to ensure water supplies and control flooding. Weather management on Nibiru is conducted with frequency regulators. On Terra an electroplated gold satellite disk crossed the skies, and through magnetic emissions that you still do not understand, the amounts of water that form cloud cover in the skies over Terra were regulated. This procedure made the Lulus think we controlled the sun, and that we were gods they must worship. Marduk went right along with this, even calling himself The Lord of the Sun, Ra, and set up temples of worship for himself all over Egypt. He was extremely vain, always wanting his own way.

Sun God, The Shining One, Possessor of Heaven and Earth, and just about every other title given to any of the gods was sooner or later acquired by Marduk. Even Enki was afraid of him. Marduk seemed to have the power to bend Enki's will, in a sort of mind control of son over father. All of Enki's strength would somehow vanish into Marduk and leave Enki powerless.

We called the Great Pyramid in Giza the *Ekur*, a word that means a house that is a like a mountain. Enki and his sons built this Ekur in Giza. Marduk laid out the site and Ningishzidda, the son of Enki and Ereshkigal, installed the Pleiadian technology within. The pyramid was the primary generator of power used in all our space vehicles, the weather satellite disks, and the communications systems. Transmissions from the Pleiades, our home planet, Nibiru, and the orbiting space station came at that time to the Ekur. Whoever controlled the Great Pyramid controlled power in the family.

Marduk and Nergal began to fight for the command of the Ekur. Marduk cloned himself into an army of fierce killing warriors, huge in stature and easily replaced. With his legions of clones, he attacked Nergal's armies and a war ensued. When the sons of Marduk managed to seize the Ekur, they were overcome by greed and ambition. Fighting even among themselves, they moved the legions toward the Spaceport which belonged to Enki's brother, Enlil. Provoking Enlil and the entire family with this outrage, the sons of Marduk began a long and bloody family war, at last splitting the family of Anu into two definite sides, the Enlilites and the Enkites.

Enlil would never allow the sons of his rival brother, Enki, to control both the Ekur and the Spaceport. He could not place all communications from the Pleiades, Nibiru, and the orbiting station in the hands of the Enkites. Enlil and his sons rose to the occasion.

Ninurta was chosen to lead the Enlilite forces against Marduk. As the son of Enlil and Ninhursag, Ninurta lived to please his father, obsessively carrying out Enlil's orders and usually succeeding. I have always found Ninurta to be a strange person, extremely self-centered with a chip on his shoulder, a sort of brat. Being the center of his mother's world had left him with a few unpleasant characteristics, and

Ninurta and I had fought savagely as children. But this time, we fought together on the same side. As the granddaughter of Enlil, I am an Enlilite by birth, and I was at last pleased to see Ninhursag's son winning battles for my side of the family.

My own father, Nannar, was also commanding armies and I insisted on getting into the battle! I had achieved the level of Golden Falcon in the mastery of arms. I actually fought at Ninurta's side, once bringing him a weapon he greatly needed. I suspect it was the only time he was ever truly glad to see me!

The War was indescribably ghastly and we used the Lulus as soldiers. Occasionally entire villages happened to be in the paths of the great radiation waves and innocent Lulus died by the thousands. Many more starved to death in Nergal's African domain because Ninurta evaporated all the waters in the rivers, and scorched the lands with plasma fire. Ninurta also used what you would call chemical warfare; the terrible Madhava Missile poisoned everything in its sight. There were many types of weapons of destruction used, but the most cunning of all was the Ruadra Weapon. It produced a hologram of vast armies of charging demons and monsters, armed with plasma guns and screeching, bloodcurdling war cries. Marduk's Lulu armies could never imagine it was only an apparition, and they turned and ran, leaving his clones to face Ninurta's legions alone.

Toward the end of the war, Ninurta managed to flood the Abzu, forcing Enki and his sons to retreat into the Great Pyramid. From the protection of the Ekur, the Enkites generated a wall of poisonous light around the complex. This wall was a force field fueled by the considerable capacities of the Great Pyramid itself. No weapon of ours could penetrate it.

Ninurta summoned my twin brother, Utu, and ordered him to cut the Ekur off from all water sources. Without water, how long could they live? Desperation forced one of Enki's younger sons to make a daring effort to escape and run for water. In his courageous attempt, the poor boy was blinded by Ninurta and his brilliant weapon. One family member actually severely harmed another; this had never occurred before. Even Marduk had used assassins to kill my husband, Dumuzi.

And so Ninhursag stepped in. She had seen enough. It was bad enough for us to slaughter her Lulus, but to kill and maim the members of our own family was intolerable. She commanded her son, Ninurta, to give her a radiation suit and then she slowly walked toward the Ekur. No one would ever dare to strike Ninhursag, not even Marduk! She is the daughter of Anu, and you can bet that Enki was feeling very nervous as she ordered him to lower the poisonous wall.

The peace negotiations began. Ninhursag informed Enki and his sons that Anu had given her the authority to put a stop to the madness. Enki was ordered to surrender immediately to Enlil. Enki looked to Marduk for consent, and Marduk relented. In those times, Marduk was still afraid of Anu.

# X

# THE EKUR

The Great Pyramid at Giza, the Ekur, is a natural collector of energies. Even without the enhancements of Pleiadian technology, any pyramid will gather and amplify the surrounding frequencies. Thus the hate and anger generated by our war was magnified by the presence of the Ekur. The atmosphere of Terra was darkened and made heavy by our hatred of one another. This new density, this lowering of frequency, was merging into and altering every living thing on Terra. In her wisdom, Ninhursag saw what was occurring, but the rest of us did not notice.

Your present-day scientists understand the magnetic field surrounding all astral bodies, which is known as the

Magnetosphere. While the Magnetosphere surrounds the entire planet, it is drawn to and concentrated at Terra's polar regions. They are also aware that the Magnetosphere protects Terra from Solar Winds, which are made of high-energy plasma particles traveling at 200 miles per second. These Solar Winds would directly bombard your planet were it not for the surrounding magnetic field which deflects the solar wind plasma.

Plasma is the most abundant material in your galaxy, and therefore a desirable energy source. Pyramids contained a Pleiadian technology presently unknown to you which accessed plasma in the Solar Winds for power. The pyramids were strategically placed around the planet and used as collectors to gather the plasma. The Ekur was the largest of these power-collectors on Terra. All of our spacecraft contain similar smaller-scale collectors. Naturally, all of the planets the Pleiadians have colonized have pyramids to collect plasma power.

The Ekur was designed to connect the Solar Winds' plasma to the magnetic field from within Terra's core. This high-energy plasma was funneled down along the pyramid's vertical axis, while the magnetism from the earth's core was directed upward along the same vertical axis. Both were concentrated into an intense coherent path, analogous to what your scientists have achieved with light in laser technology.

Thousands of what we call the Singing Stones receive and transduce this energy. There are huge shards of amber, ruby, and sapphire; tall crystals of citrine, emerald, and aquamarine stand in a harmonic order along with amethyst, diamond, and quartz. Many of the stones, such as Uzup, you would not know, as they are gathered from the Pleiadian star system.

These Singing Stones are placed sequentially in an eloquent spiral in the very center of the Ekur, and in the center of the spiral is a monolithic blue crystal. The tip of the crystal is lined up perfectly with the point of the pyramid's capstone for superb power amplification. The Singing Stones are truly wonderful to behold.

As the plasma enters from the top of the Ekur, and the magnetism enters from the earth, they meet at the blue crystal at the center. The two energies join, swirling in a massively powerful vortex in the form of a torus, a geometric form that looks like a donut or bagel. As the torus forms, the two energies become one in a beautiful, spiraling union of forces. The Torus of Magnetic Flow is consequently set into motion with one ring turning in on itself, the other out. Thus we generate perpetual motion.

The beauty of this technology is not unusual for us. The forms we Pleiadians use must be in harmony with their purpose; thus, function is never greater than form. One must reflect and be equal to the other or power is diminished. Our spacecraft and our cities are also of the most perfectly elegant beauty.

I am aware that there is a debate as to whether the outer covering of the Ekur was alabaster white or turquoise. It was both. In a period of 300,000 years we experimented with different coverings to see which one would generate the most power, but the capstone was always gold, because gold is such an excellent transducer.

After the peace agreements had been sworn, Ninurta was authorized to dismantle all of the weapons systems in the Ekur, only leaving enough power to regulate weather patterns and a few communications instruments. I followed him into the Great Pyramid. As Ninurta dismantled the Singing Stones, I asked for a few emeralds. Ninurta forbade me, sanctimoniously pointing out that all the stones had to be transferred to the new power center at Heliopolis, the domain of Enlil.

Ninurta, always rigid and unbending, lived in the shadow of my father, Nannar. They were both Enlil's sons, but my father, Nannar, is so charming and handsome, so naturally gifted, that it was obvious that Enlil preferred my father to Ninurta. Ninurta could only hope that if he continued to faithfully perform his duties, he might win Enlil's approval; thus, Ninurta was very thorough, and not much fun. Duty and integrity are wonderful qualities, but Ninurta had no sense of humor.

Enlil is rigid in his adherence to Nibiruan authority, and once Enlil had made a law on Terra, he followed it to the last letter. His brother, Enki, is more flexible, more imaginative. Enlil usually took the side of Nibiru, while Enki felt a deep love for Terra and the Lulus, and often fought for the betterment of humankind.

As part of the peace agreement, Enki made certain demands on behalf of the Lulus, who had been greatly harmed by our war. Many cities had been destroyed and the Lulus themselves had died in large numbers. Enki demanded that the ruined cities be restored and new ones created. He wanted to give the Lulus the choice to become more than slave workers; therefore, laws were made which gave the Lulus the chance to choose work based on their talents. They were given a greater variety of occupations and more creative roles in their societal structures.

Because of the devastation of the war, the sons of Enki were to be limited in their power. Marduk was furious when he found out that the Giza area and Lower Egypt were given to his half-brother Ningishzidda. Ningishzidda was viewed as neutral in the family split because he is a son of Enki, but his mother, Ereshkigal, is the granddaughter of Enlil. Marduk coveted all of Egypt. Marduk wanted the whole world.

Ninurta was given control of Sumer's new capital, Kish, which gave him even more power and further enraged Marduk. Marduk wanted Kish and the rulership of Sumer for himself. He also wanted his favorite city, Babylon. We all loved Babylon; she was so very lovely in those days, and her famous gardens were the setting for many of our most renowned festivals. The people of Babylon called me Ishtar, and in my honor they built a beautiful stone gate covered in gold and lapis lazuli. If you travel there today, you can see in the old city the remnants of the temples we all built for ourselves.

Marduk had been cut out of the most choice domains. Brooding over his losses, he decided to take a little covert action and conceived a plan to use the Lulus against the other gods.

Performing austerities—intense focusing disciplines— Marduk activated his cobra-like will. Using crystals and frequency beams, he placed thought forms into the receptive minds of the Lulus. Marduk's magic was a great success. For the first time ever, the thought occurred to the Lulus that they could be just like us! They woke in the night with a vision of a great tower climbing to the sky, and with the knowledge to build it.

The Lulus seemed to come from all over Terra as they assembled on the plains outside of Babylon. They began to construct a tower to reach heaven where they would demand equality from the gods. Very dangerous! Marduk must have thought he could later remove such nonsense from their brains. The Lord Marduk giveth, and the Lord Marduk taketh away!

In those times, the Lulus required only a very simple language. Because their vocabulary was limited to what was necessary for performing menial tasks and taking orders, complex concepts did not often enter their speech. But they still possessed remnants of their original telepathic abilities from the time of their harmony with Terra's animals, and these telepathic powers were functioning in full force as the Lulus congregated and began mysteriously to build their Tower to Heaven.

When Enlil heard of what the Lulus were doing, he hurried to the site and walked among them, warning them to stop. He told them this act was against the will of their creators, and they must stop or they would be punished. To Enlil's amazement, they ignored him. It was as if they never even saw or heard him. Enlil's heart sickened. Only a god could form this magic, and the only god he could imagine who was capable of doing such a thing was the scorned son of Enki, Marduk. Enlil knew he would have to take drastic measures and generate a force field greater than Marduk's.

Enlil destroyed the Tower of Babel with one particle beam. The Lulus never knew what hit them. Most died; those who were unfortunate enough to live experienced the agonies of radiation sickness. Plus, their memories were gone, wiped clean. Lulus staggered aimlessly, wondering where to go, or where they had come from. It was a pitiful sight. Each Lulu began to feel an invisible wall of separateness growing around his or her being as all across Terra, cities and villages were inundated by Enlil's frequencies of separation. And from that time on, all the humans were encouraged to emphasize and develop their differences. New languages were created for each region. Races began to denigrate other races, and people were taught to fear each other. The Lulus learned to hate, and they began to fight among themselves.

To add to the confusion, each god was given many different names. Men fought over whose god was the true god, when often it was the same god, only named differently. I myself became Ishtar, Venus, Hathor, Aphrodite, Lakshmi, Rhiannon, and countless more. Dissension among the Lulus was fomented. Never again would your ancestors be allowed to unite against us, and never again would the human species remember that they had all come from the same source, a wild creature from Terra and my great-aunt Nin.

My last experience with the Ekur concerns me and Marduk. You may remember that when my husband, Dumuzi, was killed, it was Marduk who was behind it. It was true that before and after the war, I had my heart set on ruling Egypt, and Dumuzi was too weak to take it from his brothers alone. Egypt was so rich, and with my help and encouragement, Egypt could have been Dumuzi's, and I would have been her queen. Marduk was determined to thwart my ambitions. I had never liked being around Marduk; his need to control everyone was so unpleasant. Even his appearance repelled me. His cruel, majestic beauty was designed solely to generate fear.

After Dumuzi's death there was an inquiry. Marduk claimed that even though he had given the order to stop Dumuzi's escape, the murder had been an unfortunate accident, the result of overzealous troops.

During the war, I had gained a reputation for courage and mastery of my weapons. Upon hearing Marduk's pathetic excuse for the murder of my husband, I lost all reason. I let it be known that I was out to get Marduk. My reputation as a zealous warrior inspired fear, and Marduk fled into the Ekur.

I flew down to the pyramids. Dressed in golden armor and brandishing my weapons, I arrogantly commanded Marduk to come out. He ignored me, something I hate, and naturally, I lost my composure. Hurling all sorts of abusive curses at Marduk, I raised my plasma beam and began to strike the sides of the Great Pyramid. The very stones of the Ekur began to shake.

I was quite a sight, barebreasted and beautiful, as I unleashed my awesome fury. I am passionate. We all made derogatory little jokes about Marduk having had his tail removed; so I called him the Great Serpent, as well as other excellent names I won't repeat here.

The other gods were getting a little nervous. My brother, Utu, decided to call Enlil, and, knowing that Anu is the only one I ever listen to, Enlil called Anu. A hologram from Anu appeared in the skies over Giza. Anu entreated me, his beloved Inanna, to cease and desist from my wrath. Anu knew that Marduk had secreted weapons in the Ekur, and did not want his Inanna to be harmed. He loves me. Anu advised me to try Marduk in a court of his fellow gods. Okay, I thought. I didn't know how I was going to break into the pyramid anyway, and I was running out of curses.

We had never had an actual trial before. Enlil had been banished for raping his future wife, but he was never tried in a courtroom. No one really knew what to do, and no one wanted to judge another god for something they might want to do themselves because the precedent for punishment could one day fall on them. Since Marduk had someone else kill Dumuzi, was his crime punishable by death? No one was willing to pronounce the death sentence on a member of the family of Anu.

It was left to me to take charge, and my adrenaline was still flowing from rattling the pyramid. I conceived the perfect punishment: seal Marduk in the Ekur, essentially bury him alive, no food and no water. Since no one else wanted to take the initiative, they all agreed to my plan. Marduk was to be buried alive in the Ekur. I was happy.

I knew that even without food and water, the energy in the pyramid would keep Marduk alive for quite awhile. This assured him of a long, drawn out, ghastly death. I was very pleased with myself. I can be so imaginative, and I had avenged Dumuzi. Not that I had been all that much in love with Dumuzi, but I had grown to hate Marduk and I wanted him out of my way for good. I was personally present for the ceremonies. They simply pulled levers and enormous blocks of stone fell into place, one upon another, sealing Marduk in his tomb.

Well, even Marduk has a mother. She was not pleased with her son's entombment and immediately began to plead with Enki. More pathetic still was Marduk's sister/wife, Sarpanit, parading herself naked in front of the Ekur day and night. She created quite a spectacle crying and beating the walls with her tiny bleeding hands. A great crowd of Lulus gathered to watch and Enki weakly gave in. He pressured me to relent. We were very friendly, Enki and I. He had, after all, given me the *Divine MEs*, so reluctantly, I agreed to the release.

I knew it was a mistake, but I couldn't argue with Enki for long, so I gave in with the concession that Marduk make offerings in all my temples to appeal for my mercy. The capstone of the Ekur was removed with powerful concentrated plasma beams and Marduk was freed. If Marduk and I had disliked each other before, you can well imagine this little incident did not improve our relationship. Perhaps he occasionally woke in the night hearing my bloodcurdling screams, "Bury him alive!!!" He was my enemy now; I knew he would eventually seek revenge. But for the time being, he was put into exile as punishment for Dumuzi's murder.

Marduk's ambitions to rule the world would not vanish so easily. One day he would be back. Dark and brooding, the red eyes of Marduk permeated my soul. I felt him waiting, plotting in silent rage.

# GILGAMESH

In the Pleiadian star system, we see ourselves as information gatherers for Prime Creator. Prime Creator *is* and we are sent out to gather experience in time and space. You may judge me by the standards of your world, but I did not judge myself. I was simply living and learning. If one experience was not fulfilling, I moved on to another.

Prime Creator manifests a womb matrix we call the Mother Goddess, and from her, many other sources of creation are brought forth. A multitude of higher beings form thought; these thoughts become sound, and sound, in turn, flows out to its own level of frequency and manifests realities.

My adventures were part of the movement of all that had been created before me. I come from a line: I am Prime Creator, the Mother Goddess, and my ancient ancestors from other dimensions and star systems. I am a part of Anu and Antu, I am Enlil and Ninhursag, and I carry my own mother and father within me. The consciousness of all that came before me, I express in my power to create.

In that time on Terra, I did not see that my actions could harm the Lulus and their future generations—you. I certainly did not know such harm would flow back into my life and build The Wall.

After Anu gave me the Right to Grant Kingship, I commuted back and forth between Uruk and the Indus Valley. Grains and other commodities flowed abundantly along my trade routes, my priestesses became richer by the day, and everyone was happy. Still, I had no husband.

I was in the same boat as my great-aunt Nin. There was no one suitably placed for me to marry. Over the years I had watched Ninhursag become more and more withdrawn and rigid, and I did not want to end up like her. I'm not the old-maid type, and I felt like a loose cannon on deck. I was so beautiful, and only a little ruthless. What was I to do?

In order to deal with this little problem, I resolved to combine the rituals of Kingship and Sacred Marriage. In this lovely ceremony, the future king became my husband for one night. The temple was covered with flowers and bathed in candlelight. The scent of the flowers and the sounds of sweet music filled the temple halls. I was dressed in silks, crowned with a golden tiara, and led by the priests and priestesses to the sacred bed where my beloved was waiting.

I had many children in this manner and created many royal lineages from these ceremonies. I, who had no real husband of my own race, could enjoy the wedding ceremony over and over. The Sacred Marriage Ceremony was very popular with the Lulus. These ceremonies made them love me, and thus I gained power over the cities.

This custom of having children with the Lulus was continually practiced by the men in the family of Anu. Enki couldn't begin to count how many lovers he enjoyed or the number of children he fathered. My father, Nannar, and my brother, Utu, were no different. I merely formalized a common practice into an elaborate ritual, and the Sacred Marriage Ceremony made me a popular favorite with the Lulus.

The ritual of the Sacred Marriage also allowed me to create men powerful enough to be interesting to me. I taught them wisdom, knowledge, and magic. The surest way to transfer these frequencies is the act of sexual union performed with the highest consciousness and great focus. I am a natural at this sort of thing, and many men benefited from these initiations.

The DNA of the Lulus was strengthened and amplified by my genetic infusion. Unknowingly, I also tied myself into the lineages of thousands of human beings and, thus, their future lives. My genes wove themselves into a river of people without my knowing I was becoming a part of them.

You know how it is, you are sitting around, mildly bored, wanting something exciting to happen, and by synchronicity, you are drawn into a new world. Without any conscious thought of where it will lead, the promise of fresh, new experience draws you, and the fabric of time catches you in her web. So I, likewise, was forever drawn into Terra's web and the lives of her inhabitants.

My brother, Utu, was quite happily married to his wife, Aya, and I would occasionally visit them. Utu and I were always very close, and I know he loves me, but he was so busy with all the shuttles going back and forth from Terra to the Space Station that we barely had time to see each other. Aya was all wrapped up in her children, their schools and clothes. Ninurta and his wife, Gula, were the same. Gula only talked about her children. Ninurta had so many duties that he and Gula did not even see each other that frequently. I admired these women for their devotion to their children, but it just wasn't enough for me. I couldn't wait to get back to the temples and check the commodity reports. The Sacred Marriage Ceremony gave me the freedom to pursue my business interests, along with the pleasures of many husbands and many children.

My Sacred Marriages attracted men from all over Terra. I would watch the men who came into the temples and make inquiries about their abilities and intelligence, and I became accustomed to picking out the best as they pleased me. Then one day I met a man who rejected my advances— Gilgamesh!

Gilgamesh had been made Fifth Ruler of the dynasty in Uruk by my brother, Utu. I was away on business at the time in the Indus Valley, and Utu was anxious to grant kingship to Gilgamesh. Utu felt a strong affection for him because Gilgamesh was of Utu's lineage. Utu had at one time felt a strong affection for one of my temple priestesses, and their union had produced a male who was so desirable that he, in turn, mated with a pure Nibiruan lady. Their son was Gilgamesh, and he claimed himself to be two-thirds god and one-third human, a claim he felt gave him certain rights.

Gilgamesh was exceedingly handsome, what you

might call a hunk, and he was very popular with the people. Gilgamesh was loved by all, and Utu doted on this hero king who carried my brother's blood in his veins.

Highly intelligent, Gilgamesh began to learn all he could about the history of Terra and the family of Anu. The more he learned, the more he became obsessed with the thought of his mortality. Gilgamesh did not want to die. After all, he reasoned, he was two-thirds god and should, therefore, be immortal like Utu and the other gods. He begged his mother and his grandfather, Utu, to help him. Utu basically told him to forget it, the other gods would not allow it, and Gilgamesh should be enjoying the time allotted to him.

Dismayed and depressed, Gilgamesh began to drink heavily. He went on binges eating, drinking, copulating, and challenging any and all to fight him. Gilgamesh was desperate to distract himself from the fear of death. His erratic behavior and violent outbursts disrupted the normal flow of life in Uruk.

The gods felt that something must be done to calm Gilgamesh down. Gilgamesh needed a friend, a peer, and in the wilderness there lived a man named Enkidu. Enkidu was one of Enki's genetic experiments, and a match in physical strength for Gilgamesh. The gods decided to capture Enkidu as a companion for Gilgamesh.

Enkidu was still wild in his nature, and in the innocent state of telepathy with the animals of the steppes and forests. In order to capture Enkidu, the gods sent one of my priestesses to seduce him. Enkidu had never seen anything quite like this lovely woman. Enthralled by her enticing body, he was overcome with lust and copulated with her again and again. For seven days and nights in the trance of ecstatic passion, Enkidu lost himself in the sea of her beauty.

When he was finally satiated, he looked around for his animal friends. But they no longer knew him and, as he attempted to come near them, they fled his presence, running in fear. Enkidu was forever changed.

Feeling lost and alone, with nowhere to go, poor Enkidu timidly followed the priestess into Uruk, where he was given to Gilgamesh. Gilgamesh and Enkidu began their friendship by wrestling each other, testing the depths of each other's strength. When Enkidu proved he was a match for Gilgamesh, the two bonded in brotherhood.

Gilgamesh shared his fear of death with his new friend. Enkidu was moved to tears by Gilgamesh's self-pity and spoke of a place he had come upon with the gazelles in the Land of the Cedars, the secret Abode of the Gods; there Gilgamesh could demand immortality. A terrible monster named Humbaba had been created by Enlil to stand guard in his domain, the Land of the Cedars. Enkidu told Gilgamesh they would have to fight the Humbaba to gain entrance into the Abode. Excited by the prospect of a new challenge, the two set off in high spirits.

The Abode of the Gods exists in a different dimension than Terra, but may be entered through a Time Portal in the Land of the Cedars. Terra vibrates at a different frequency than Nibiru, and we can only enter the vibration of Terra through such Time Portals, as they are the gates to travel between dimensions. The Humbaba was a holographic monster concealing a deadly weapon which guarded this entrance. We, as Pleiadians, must also return to our own time frequency regularly, or we will age at the same rate as humans. Because one year on Nibiru is equivalent to 3,600 years on Terra, we appear as immortals to you.

Utu and I watched from the sky as Gilgamesh and Enkidu approached the Time Portal and began to attack the

Humbaba. We were so impressed by their courage, we decided to play with the hologram and let them think they had beheaded the thing. Afterward, we would usher them back to Uruk with no harm done.

Thinking the Humbaba safely dead, Gilgamesh and Enkidu lay exhausted by a stream. Gilgamesh was all sweaty from the battle and he took off his clothes to wash. Well, that did it! He was so beautiful, with his long black hair and a chiseled body glistening with manliness, that I was overwhelmed with desire. I wanted him.

From my ship hovering over him, I cried out, "Oh, Gilgamesh, I long to feel your strong arms around my slim waist and to delight in the sweet joys of your manhood." I also offered him gold and lands, power and fame, the usual.

You can imagine my shock when he refused. He even insulted me, going on and on about how I had turned this man into a frog, and that one into a wolf. He raved on saying terrible things about me, that I was like a shoe that bit the owner's foot and other rude insults. It wasn't my fault that I out lived all the men who were my lovers! He even offered to recount the list of my previous lovers' names!

No one had ever dared to speak to me in this repulsive manner, and hell has no fury like a woman scorned! I wasn't putting up with this from any man, even if he was two-thirds god. I went straight to Anu and began to complain. Luckily, Antu was there.

Anu tried to calm me down, but he also pointed out that what Gilgamesh had said was partially true. Well, perhaps I had lost interest rather quickly in a few of my lovers, but I couldn't remember turning anyone into a frog. Besides, I am Inanna, Queen of Heaven, beloved of Anu, and no one talks to me like that!

Sweetly and slowly I begged Anu to give me a weapon

to trounce Gilgamesh with, a big radiation weapon. And if Anu wouldn't give me the weapon, I rashly threatened to unleash all sorts of astral terrors from other dimensions. Anu knew I was just trying to convince him to appease me and give me what I wanted.

Anu reminded me that the use of such a powerful radiation weapon would poison the crops. He wondered if I had enough grain in storage for my people, and when I told him that I did, he gave in.

I now see that occasionally I did have a foul temper. This time, my brother, Utu, was completely against me. Gilgamesh was of his blood, and Utu dearly loved the boy. Utu arranged to have the radiation weapon malfunction, which must have secretly pleased Anu.

I was furious at having my plans for revenge wrecked, and I made a formal complaint. Anu conferred with his son, Enlil, who decided that Gilgamesh and Enkidu must be punished for attacking the Humbaba, thus defying the weapons of the gods. Anu suggested death, but Enlil wasn't willing to see Gilgamesh die and he compromised by offering to kill Enkidu alone.

Enkidu wasn't up to having his death negotiated so coldly, and he fell into a coma. While poor Enkidu lay ill and unconscious, Gilgamesh became even more obsessive over his own death. Gilgamesh took to weeping and bewailing his own fate, barely noticing his sick friend. This complete narcissistic selfishness convinced me that Gilgamesh really was one of us, a true child of the family of Anu!

The gods, in their compassion, took pity on Enkidu and commuted his death sentence to life spent slaving in the mines, a fate from which there was no return. No Lulu ever returned from Ereshkigal's UnderWorld. Lucky Enkidu.

As for Gilgamesh, his increased desperation made him

decide to press his grandfather, Utu, for further help. He became more determined than ever to seek the Immortality of the Gods, something many humans have similarly desired.

# XII

# UTU AND THE SERPENT TUNNELS

When Anu first began to colonize Terra over 500,000 years ago, thousands of miles of underground tunneling already existed. These tunnels and caves were dug by the Dragon People and the Snake People. Anu fought not only for Terra in those early days, but also for these tunnels, which are of crucial strategic value because they hold the Time Portals. As we exist in a different time frequency, none of us can enter the dimension of Terra without using the Time Portals.

The treaty that settled the war between the Enkites and the Enlilites gave the entire Sinai Peninsula to my father, Nannar. This area held the Mission Control Center, the Spaceport, and the entrance to the tunnels. As the son of Nannar, my twin brother, Utu, was given command over these facilities.

Utu is the soul of devotion to duty, and our grandfather, Enlil, trusted him completely. Utu and I have always loved each other very much and, because we are twins, we are telepathically linked, but Utu is much more like my mother, Ningal, than I am. Utu has a quiet intelligence, a nature of dignity and humility. I am more like my father, Nannar, adventurous and passionate. My father could charm anyone with his dark mysterious gaze.

Utu, as I have said, was exceptionally fond of Gilgamesh, and truly wanted to help him. After Enkidu was dragged off to work in the mines for the rest of his life, Utu paid Gilgamesh a visit. Well, Gilgamesh got right into begging Utu for the Immortality of the Gods!

Utu suggested to Gilgamesh that if he could somehow prove his worthiness to the other gods, perhaps he might be granted at least an extended life. After all, Enlil had granted Noah immortality. So Utu transmitted visions of Tilmun, the Land of the Living, to Gilgamesh in his dreams so as not to arouse the ire of the other gods.

Tilmun is the Land of the Living because it is outside of Earth time and the dimension of Terra. As I have mentioned, we must leave the time frequencies of Terra on a regular cyclical basis. If we did not, our bodies would eventually become bonded to Terra and we would age as humans do. We all traveled periodically to Tilmun, and had quite beautiful homes there. To reach Tilmun one must travel through the Snake Tunnels.

The tunnels themselves are wonderful. Originally formed by the snake worms, the tunnels flow as concentric circles in endless turns. The light in these places glows a greenish gold and shows the walls to be glistening with a slimy substance. The slime is merely a sealant, but it repulses humans well enough. Many miles of the tunnels are left in total darkness.

Only very rarely have humans found their way to these tunnels. In order to find the entrances and enter them, one must evoke *snake energy* or what you call *kundalini* or the *chi*. Without mastery of these subtle forces, an entrance remains invisible. Terra's mythology is full of stories of such places. Some humans have stumbled upon them unknowingly in altered states, but few of those ever returned. The shamans of the so-called primitive tribes of Terra have frequently gained entry, but they prefer to remain silent about such things.

In your present time, there are seven entrances to the tunnels. One is located under the Sphinx in Egypt, and another is in Jerusalem. A third entrance is at the bottom of the Pacific Ocean near an area named Vanuata. Lake Titicaca in Peru, Mount Shasta in California, and Mount Meru in the Himalayas hold three more. The seventh entrance lies under the thick ice of Antarctica. Antarctica is also the location of a magnetic torus which powers all the tunnels with plasma energy.

In dreams, Utu told Gilgamesh that by entering the Serpent Tunnels he would find Tilmun, the Land of the Living, where Noah, the survivor of the Great Flood, lived. If Gilgamesh could find Noah, perhaps Noah would give him the secret of immortality. Since the tunnels were his domain, Utu planned to help Gilgamesh through by projecting a few useful holograms into Gilgamesh's brain to urge him along.

I myself was pretty bored by the whole Gilgamesh affair, which wasn't an affair at all for me! But Utu couldn't stop himself from telling me every detail of poor Gilgamesh's journey. Utu watched each step his precious grandson took. Later, the Lulus shared his avid interest and the legend of Gilgamesh's search for immortality became very popular. It illustrated all their fears, hopes and defeats. If Gilgamesh could not hope to live forever, then who of their race could?

Enki, in the early days of colonizing Terra, had expanded the tunnels. Enki found the worm method too slow, so he used anti-matter beams to evaporate the rock. In places, this process left large bubbles on the walls which reflect light in an eerie manner. Enki loved them and was quite pleased with his bubble tunnels. Enki was always coming up with these genetic mutant things in his laboratory in the Abzu, so he created quantities of ugly monsters to guard the tunnel entrances which lead to other dimensions.

With a little help from Utu, Gilgamesh crossed the mountains and reached the entrance to one of the tunnels. There he ran into some of Enki's scorpion guards, monsters with human legs and scorpion-like heads and bodies. They gave Gilgamesh quite a shock. The scorpion guards warned Gilgamesh of the endless dark tunnels which became a maze of death for most humans, and refused to let him enter. Then, as if by magic, Utu gave the signal to let Gilgamesh pass.

For what seemed like an eternity, Gilgamesh wandered in total darkness through the tunnel maze, bumping into walls, bruising his body and calling out wildly to Utu. The air was so thick that Gilgamesh could barely breathe, but hour after hour, he continued his journey. He began to think himself mad as he imagined all sorts of terrible demons shoving him against the slimy walls. All sense of direction was lost and blackness became his only reality.

Then something extraordinary happened. Gilgamesh

began to see in the darkness, but not in his normal way; rather, he saw with the eye of a god. The genes he had inherited from Utu had begun to activate the cones of Gilgamesh's eyes. At first he saw only subtle golden outlines of the bubble walls, like an infrared picture, and even though he still walked in complete blackness, the outlines were vivid enough to guide him on and prevent him from battering his body on the walls.

Emerging from the tunnel, Gilgamesh entered the garden of the gods. At first he was dazed, but soon began to refresh himself with fruit and water. Gilgamesh was in one of my great-grandmother Antu's famous gardens. She built these things not only on Nibiru, but anywhere Anu would let her. There are many legends concerning these gardens because, aside from real fruits and flowers, there is always the section formed of gold and precious stones. Imagine grape vines wrought from gold and silver with grapes of amethyst and peridot. Rows of golden wheat and corn abounded, and among a plethora of artistic perfections, the roses were the most wondrous. Antu had made this art form into a Pleiadian passion and the noblewomen competed with each other in centenary competitions by projecting holograms of their gardens across the galaxies.

Gilgamesh, bloody and dirty from his ordeal in the tunnel, was properly awed. Utu spoke to him, suggesting a bath in the garden pool, and then directed his traveler to a veiled female seated on the edge of the sea, named Siduri. Siduri of the Dragon race serves the gods wine before they cross the sea to reach their homes. Gilgamesh asked her how he might find Noah.

Siduri explained that this sea was uncrossable by any human. For a Lulu, this sea was known as the waters of death. Gilgamesh told Siduri his entire story, and restated his claim to be two-thirds god, while Utu hovered above them. Seeing Utu, Siduri called the boatman to take Gilgamesh to the abode of Noah.

The old man, Noah, relived his memories of the Great Flood for his guest, emphasizing the fact that it was the gods themselves who had determined to destroy the Lulus. Having learned much about the gods over the centuries, Noah knew we were not to be trusted, and he warned Gilgamesh to give up his quest for immortality.

But Gilgamesh would not be convinced to give up, so Noah suggested that Gilgamesh perform austerities to prove his worthiness to the gods. Perhaps if Gilgamesh could stay awake and vigilant for a week, he would impress the gods, and they might grant his request. Thus poor Gilgamesh sat down to prove himself, but immediately fell fast asleep.

Exasperated, Noah then told Gilgamesh of a plant that grew on the bottom of the sea which might make him immortal. Valiantly, Gilgamesh dove down into the water and brought the plant into the boat, only to have it stolen by a snake. The Immortality of the Gods was forever lost to Gilgamesh, even with all of Utu's help.

Utu was heartbroken, but there was nothing left my brother could do for Gilgamesh. It was the law: the Lulus must remain in a state of unawareness, a kind of sleep. Eons ago genetic manipulations had taken their divinity from them. Even Utu's love for Gilgamesh could not change that. Gilgamesh returned to Uruk, where he ruled until his death, and where he was known as the one who had seen the tunnels.

# XIII

# SARGON THE GREAT

Sargon was the love of my life on Terra, and together we made beautiful love, beautiful babies, and great kingdoms. I first saw him in my temple. Sargon was the cup-bearer to Ur-Zababa, the king of the city of Kish. I noticed him because he bore a remarkable resemblance to my father, Nannar. He definitely had Nannar's eyes. Even though no one ever knew exactly who Sargon's father was, I had my suspicions.

Sargon's mother was a high priestess in one of my Love Temples. Upon his birth, she wrapped him in blankets in a basket of rushes and set him on the river. Praying, she carefully watched as he floated past a man named Akki who was in charge of irrigating the fields with water from the river. Akki pulled Sargon from the waters, adopted him as his son, and taught Sargon to tend his garden. As Sargon grew to be a man, his natural leadership abilities brought him to the court of Kish, but it was his beauty and humor that drew me to love him. He was tall and strong, with high cheekbones and a gentle touch. Highly intelligent, his very being commanded loyalty.

I was drawn to him from the first moment we met and, most wonderfully, Sargon felt the same. Electricity surged through our bodies. He was not afraid of me, or shy. Knowing what I wanted, he took me like a god, and our lovemaking was divine. In our beginning, for a fortnight and more we remained in an ecstatic state. We secured the golden doors to my bedchambers with Sargon's mighty sword, and only occasionally allowed my servants to bring us wines and supper. Not needing food, we lived on the nectar of our love and passion.

Our only desire was to lie entwined in each other's arms for hours simply touching, exploring the newly found territory of our bodies with our lips and fingertips. Our longing eyes searched deeply into one another as if we might have once been together, and then somehow lost each other. As we lost ourselves in union, we grew stronger together and became as one.

Sometimes in the gentle afternoons, we would bathe in my garden pools under fruit trees in dappled sunlight. I wore nothing but my jewels. Necklaces of gold, lapis lazuli and pearls cascaded over my breasts, a chain of diamonds encircled my slim waist, and emerald bracelets adorned my wrists and ankles. Seated in the warm waters with fragrant flowers floating beside us, Sargon would tenderly kiss my body, caressing my firm, full breasts, taking his sweet time to arouse the powerful force of my passion until I would softly entreat him to enter me.

His manhood brought me completion as waves of

pleasure rippled through my very being. Our two bodies seemed to dissolve, pulsating into white light as we became as one in an ocean of timeless creation. The consciousness of two as one stood in the vast silence of eternity, and our pleasure became music in the higher realms.

Sargon adored me, and I made him my King. Because everything we touched prospered, flowered, and flourished, we built a new kingdom which we named Akkad. There we designed and created a beautiful new city, Agade.

In Agade we built a wonderful temple dedicated to me and named it Ulmesh, which meant luxurious and glittering, as it surely was. I instructed musicians to play night and day in my temple. Our people were happy and prosperous; their houses were built of lapis and silver. Our storehouses were piled high with grain and fruits. Old people were revered, women honored, and our young were radiant with the beauty of confidence. Little children played happily in this city of love. Sargon the Great and his beloved Inanna ruled the magic kingdom of Akkad, and it was a wonderful period of time for me.

Once Akkad was securely established, I began to encourage Sargon to take over more lands. The Lulus had been fighting among themselves, and I convinced my brother, Utu, that a consolidation under Sargon would bring a time of peace and plenty from which we would all benefit. Utu met with our father, Nannar, and grandfather, Enlil. Enlil liked Sargon immensely. Perhaps Sargon reminded him of his own son, Nannar. Whatever the reason, Enlil granted Sargon Kingship over all of Sumer, as well as Akkad. We created a new script to record our accomplishments, called Akkadian.

I could never have made such far-reaching conquests without the approval of Enlil. In later years, it appears I was to forget this cold, hard fact.

The time of Sargon in your counting is 2334–2279 BC. His rule was a time of great glory for me. In those days, I was the reigning Queen of Heaven and Terra! Enlil permitted Sargon to conquer the known world from Egypt to India, and we formed alliances and trade agreements with Ninurta, Nergal, and Ningishzidda. Grains and wine, copper and gold, and all manner of goods flowed freely along trade routes. Our people became rich, and even the gods seemed to be content. But in keeping with the human flaw of hubris, Sargon made a terrible mistake. I saw it coming; power had gone to his head. He began to think he was equal to the gods and sadly, he began to drink to excess.

Sargon and I had borne a lovely girl whose name was Enheduanna. She was like me, beautiful and headstrong. Enheduanna had a gift for poetry, and spent hours composing hymns to her father's greatness, his conquests, and his physical beauty. She was in love with her father, and determined to put a wedge between Sargon and me.

I could not blame her for her feelings; there was no one in her world to match her father. But her constant attentions had an insidious effect on Sargon. She became a priestess so she would not have to marry, and she waited for Sargon in the temple. Filling his aging ego with dreams of youth and virility, she recited her poems and poured him wine. Sargon desperately wanted to perform some heroic act to please his daughter.

There was a temple in Babylon whose foundation soil had been consecrated and designated as sacred to Marduk. This consecrated soil was Marduk's way of keeping his claws on Babylon during his period of exile. He had always been touchy and possessive about Babylon.

Sargon conceived a ceremony in which he removed this sacred soil to a new location, where it would serve as the symbolic foundation for a new Babylon—which Sargon would build. Little did he know that this act would turn fate against him. When Marduk heard of this sacrilege, he moved the Pasupata Plasmon weapon into his spacecraft and flew over the fields of Akkad and Sumer. Waves of high-intensity radiation destroyed the crops in a matter of minutes, and the ensuing period of famine caused our people to revolt against Sargon. Sargon was forced to put down hundreds of rebellions. Men who had once worshipped and loved him raised their swords against him, and praise turned to curses as the starving Lulus watched their children die in their arms. Our empire began to disintegrate.

I was not aging, and Sargon was. He began to crumble before my eyes. I could only watch in horror as the drinking became a nightmare. He even began to curse me, his beloved Inanna. Sargon moved into the temple to be near Enheduanna. At night, I lay alone in the huge cedar bed we had built for us. As gentle breezes blew the white silk curtains across our bed, the now-painful memories of our magnificent passion tormented me and a cold loneliness gripped my heart. I could not let everything we had built slip away—the peaceful times, the beautiful cities. I had to face my fate alone; I had to fight. I would not lose what Sargon and I had built, no matter the cost.

The sight of Sargon lying on his deathbed trembling in sweat, with Enheduanna by his side, remains burned in my memory to this day. Could this be the same man whose strength had brought me to ecstasy, the same man I had crowned as King, as my equal? For me, Sargon's end was a tragedy that changed my life forever. I was never the same. A part of me died that day; the exuberant little girl who ran laughing across lapis floors was forever gone.

There was no prince to rescue me or my people. I knew it was up to me to take what was mine, and I was fully aware that the other gods would rush to claim my lands if I did not fight. I put on the garments of war and paraded through the legions of my soldiers upon my pet lion. Rallying my troops, I summoned up great war cries from deep within me. My soldiers were thrilled. The goddess Inanna herself was to lead them into battle. I fought beside them like a man as I became the goddess of death and destruction. I led my devoted armies into battle for two years. I killed men by the thousands.

One after the other, I placed the sons of Sargon on the throne to rule in my absence. Enheduanna wrote poems describing my massacres, saying her mother, Inanna, made the rivers run with blood. Fiercely fighting for what I believed to be mine, I upset the equilibrium of the gods. In the house of Enlil, a meeting was called. Enlil and Ninurta came to a decision: Inanna must be stopped. The gods decided to allow Marduk to return to Babylon. Enlil and Ninurta knew Marduk would be happy to curtail the activities of Inanna; I, who had sentenced Marduk to be buried alive. As the old saying goes, the enemy of my enemy is my friend.

Marduk had not forgotten being trapped in the Great Pyramid at Giza when Utu cut off the entire water supply, and on arriving in Babylon, he immediately took steps to protect the city's source of water, the Euphrates River. Marduk's engineering efforts diminished water supplies to the surrounding cities, which aggravated the other gods. They called Nergal from Africa to go to his brother,

Marduk, and speak with him.

Nergal took leave of my darling sister, Ereshkigal, and journeyed to Babylon. Nergal entered the house of Marduk and began to flatter his brother. What a great feat of engineering Marduk had achieved; however, it must be acknowledged that redirecting the Euphrates River had robbed the other gods' cities of water. Anu and Enlil had become upset.

Marduk countered that ever since the Great Flood, the balance of power on Terra had been unacceptably changed, artificially redistributed, and not to Marduk's liking. Certain weapons and power sources had been wrongly stolen from their father, Enki. Marduk demanded that these should rightly be returned to him, and not to Nergal. Marduk then threatened to poison the entire Euphrates River system if his demands were not met.

I could see an opportunity in my path. I had always been very fond of Nergal, who was so smart, so handsome. I always thought it was a shame to waste him on my sister, Ereshkigal. Enki had lost control of his boys years ago, and Nergal and Marduk were now on the verge of a real brotherly quarrel. If I could make an alliance with Nergal, perhaps he would serve my ambitions. So, I prepared a quiet supper for my brother-in-law. Nergal seemed happy to attend. We were in perfect agreement, we made plans, we made love.

The family of Anu was self-centered and narcissistic. Driven solely by our own interests, it was easy to move us to war or peace, whichever benefited us in the moment. Deep in the throes of ambition, we lost sight of character, and we forgot the simple truth that character is destiny.

The following day, Nergal returned to the house of Marduk in Babylon and an agreement was negotiated. Nergal would return the weapons and the Singing Stones to Marduk, but Marduk must leave Babylon and fly to the

Land of the Mines in Africa to retrieve them for himself. Reluctantly, Marduk agreed.

Before his departure, Marduk warned Nergal not to touch any of the controls which regulated the Euphrates River. Siblings being what they are, the moment Marduk was out of sight, Nergal broke into the control room, but much to Nergal's surprise, he discovered the entire room had been booby-trapped. As Nergal dismantled the controls, poisons were released into the river. Marduk had also engineered a mechanism which fouled the weather-regulating satellites if anyone destroyed his control facility.

The skies above Babylon turned black. Great storms raged, the rivers became contaminated, and the whole area of Akkad and Sumer was devastated. The river systems of Sumer were loved by Enki; he could not bear the sight of the poisoned Euphrates. Angered terribly, he blamed his son, Nergal, for this destructive mischief. Nergal reacted to his father's anger by refusing to erect a statue of Enki that had already been planned. Just to make a point, and at my suggestion, Nergal burned down Marduk's house!

With Marduk in Africa, at least for the moment, I placed the grandson of Sargon, Narim-sin, upon the throne of Akkad. My father, Nannar, adored this boy and Nergal also favored him. My alliance with Nergal, based on Nergal's enmity with his brother, Marduk, gave me enough power that Narim-sin and I were able to continue to wage war and conquer territories for a time.

I suppose I was getting a little rough around the edges, and the brutality of war was changing me. Some of the stories about me were not true, others were. I did deliver captured slaves to the work camps. Driven by anger, ambition, and my loneliness, I had become heartless. I felt and behaved like a cornered she-wolf. The actions of my life were beginning to show on my face; my beauty was becoming hard and cruel. I put on more paint, but it did not help. I was short-tempered and irritable, except when I wanted something, and I became manipulative to achieve what I wanted. I was a shrew, a beauty turned into a beast.

Narim-sin was very successful, and his campaigns are written about on the clay tablets. But one day we went too far. We reached the Cedar Mountains of Lebanon, too close to the Spaceport. Enlil called the gods together and they all agreed, Inanna had begun the war and must be stopped. No one stood up for me. A warrant for my arrest was issued!

I wasn't going to allow Enlil to put me in chains, so I escaped in my ship. Enlil's troops marched into my temple in Agade, and, finding me gone, took all the weapons and power sources. I hid in Nergal's palace in Ethiopia where he contacted me every day for a briefing on what was happening.

The story that I had defied Anu was circulated among the gods. This was a lie, but it gave Enlil the excuse he needed. As punishment for defying Anu, the city of Agade would be destroyed, annihilated! The beautiful silver and lapis city that Sargon and I had built was to be vaporized. The Anti-Matter Beams were brought forth, and Agade vanished. To this day, no one has discovered where my beloved Agade once existed.

Enlil, in his usual thorough manner, brought in his mountain men, the Gutian Hordes, to take back all of Akkad. Those who were loyal to me were slaughtered. Without me to lead them, my legions became demoralized and fled into the steppes.

In the palace of Nergal, I was seized by a depression I had never before experienced. Defeat and loss imprinted their ugly faces upon my body as I sat slumped on my throne for days at a time, and no one was able to get me to speak or eat.

I dreamed I was crawling through a desert. My beloved Ninhursag called out to me by the nickname she had called me as a little girl, "Nini! Nini!" I saw the sad face of Dumuzi, the husband I had not loved. The murderous laughter of Ereshkigal, my sister, echoed through me. For a moment I felt the tender caress of Sargon, only to find myself alone in a bed of snakes. Running scared through an icy night, I found myself caught in a web with a monstrous spider whose red eyes and sharp talons were poised, ready to devour me. I woke screaming...screaming.

Was I, Inanna, vulnerable? Was I so different from the slaves I had captured, or the women who brought me golden cups of wine? Was I somehow limited in my power? Why was I even here, living in this blue body?

My mother, Ningal, sent me a message begging me to come home. She promised me I would be safe in her home, safe in her arms. She gave me her word that my father, Nannar, had guaranteed my protection from any possible charges, saying I had been punished enough. She was praying for me to come home, but I must give up my innovative, adventurous ways.

Gladly, I journeyed to Ur, home to my sweet mother, Ningal. I, Inanna, once Queen of Heaven, went home to my mother.

# XIV

# TARA

What does a girl do when she has lost everything? After a time of crying myself to sleep in my mother's arms, I began to feel foolish. Here I was, Inanna, Queen of Heaven, hiding in my parents' house. As I began to heal, I became a little self-conscious and embarrassed. I began to contemplate for the first time the meaning of my life and what I had created. Deep within my soul I was feeling such anguish, and I wondered if others had felt as I did then. It was very strange and new to me.

I called my friend, Matali, daily and we had long talks. Matali was considered the top plasma energy engineering specialist, a physicist who could fix anything. He still occasionally flew Enki's spacecraft out of friendship, but he had long ago become disenchanted with the ways of the gods. Matali had married Tara, and had gone to live with her people to begin a new life.

Tara was of the ancient race of the Snake People, the Nagas, a race that lived on Terra eons before my family. The Snake People came from a different sector of the galaxy, from Altair, to live in the center of Terra. Matali suggested that I come with him and Tara to the Snake Kingdom. He thought the change would be good for me, and Tara was happy to have me, so they came for me at my mother's and we flew away.

Tara and I had become great friends in the Indus Valley, where she had taught my priestesses the arts of dance. Tara was taught the art of sky dancing by the *apsarases*, the dancers of heaven, and she was a master. Through intense concentration, she was able to lift her slim body up into the air and perform celestial movements of the utmost elegance and grace. From the tips of her fingers to the softly singing golden bells on her ankles, Tara's dance is an exquisite expression of feeling.

I love Tara so! Seeing my forlorn self, she wrapped her arms around me and began to weep. "Oh! My dear friend," she cried. For a moment my pride held on to me, but soon I, too, was weeping. Tara's beauty was not only physical, it came from within her. She possessed a quiet balance of being, a gentle wisdom, that made you want to be with her. No wonder Matali loved her. Matali gazed lovingly at us crying in each others arms as our ship climbed into the skies and headed for a Time Portal.

The Kingdom of the Snake People is vast indeed. There are many cities inside Terra, each resplendent with towers of white alabaster. The air is fresh, regulated by extensive systems powered by energy sources at the poles of Terra. There are gardens and crop fields which abundantly provide for the people. The Snake People have a variety of body types: some are human-like, some are half-snake or reptilian. They can see in the darkness, and they can access a group mind if they so desire, with their telepathic abilities.

As the days passed in the Kingdom of the Snake People, I questioned Tara endlessly, entreating her to tell me her secrets. What gave her such integrity and beauty? How could I attain her magical state? Tara told me of many things, of how her people had come to this planet long ago to build their underground cities and tunnels. She told me there was only one among them who knew everything, and that one was called The Wise One, the Old Serpent Woman.

I implored Tara to take me to this being, and arrangements were made for Tara, Matali, and I to journey together to the abode of the Old Serpent Woman. Her name is unpronounceable in your present language—it is a sound, a sound that *feels* of Love. From her shoulders down, she is a woman; but from her shoulders up she has the head of a serpent. She emanates an energy I had never felt before and have not felt since. She is neither old nor young, and when you try to fix your gaze on something solid in her, she constantly transforms before your eyes. One minute she is exquisite beauty, the next, a raging demon; and yet, one is never afraid in her presence. It is as if she embodies all that *is*, and that is all right.

As I sat before her, she nodded to me, knowing what I desired. She knew who I was and all that I had done. She seemed to know me even beyond my life as Inanna. It was as though we had always known each other, as if I had somehow always been inside her mind. She looked into me with familiar wonder and compassion. She showed no desire to control me or manipulate me; rather, she found joy in my adventures, in my delight, and radiated her unconditional love.

Gradually everything around us turned into golden

pulsating light, time began to melt, and I felt the dimensions merge. In the Eye of my Mind I saw that Terra had existed for eons. There had been three spheres in this place in the galaxy, and this present Terra was the third. At the end of each great cycle, the sphere had been destroyed and a new planet created in its place.

I saw a vision from the time of the first Terra. This time was more gentle and subtle than the one of the Nibiruan colony. There was great Love on the planet, and the beings who existed there devoted themselves to returning to Prime Creator.

I saw a day in that time, oceans of hillsides with great crowds of people all dressed in white seated along the slopes. At the top of a hill stood a white marble pavilion with tall columns, and under the columns in a crescent row were twelve couples, male and female. They began to chant: "IIIliiii...OHhhhh...AHhhh..." Over and over these tones flowed out and down the hillside until all was vibrating in sound. There were a multitude of bright-faced entities toning the same frequencies, and as the energy rose, the beings began to turn into light. At first, light only surrounded their bodies, but soon their bodies *were* light. Every man, woman, and child on those hills became light. As their frequencies continued pulsating and ascending, the sound formed into a spiral. Angels and other higher dimensional beings were drawn into the spiraling light by these building energies. Finally, Prime Creator breathed the spiral into Itself as joy radiated throughout the Universe.

In our state of ecstasy and bliss, we had witnessed a mass ascension of life joyfully returning to its source, Prime Creator. Somehow Tara, Matali, and I were there in that marble pavilion, and yet we were still sitting in the presence of the Old Serpent Woman. It was as if the separation of the eons did not exist, as if we were in both times and places simultaneously. Tears of happiness streamed down our faces.

In our hearts we thanked the Old Serpent Woman and took leave of her. Our bodies were charged with electrical force, and it was enough for one day.

Back in the realm of the gods, Marduk was plotting and planning. Nergal had not given up and was creating alliances with the Enlilites, the enemies of his father, Enki. The rivalry of the sons of Enki and the sons of Enlil built up in the atmosphere of Terra. From deep in the Serpent Kingdom, we watched as the gods moved ever closer to their destruction.

# XV

# GANDIVA

Enki's sons had grown up knowing that all of Terra would have belonged to them if it had not been for Enlil and his sons. Enki's own bitterness and animosity toward his brother, Enlil, had seeped into their lives like a poison. The Enkites, passionately determined to avenge themselves, opposed Enlil's every move. As Enki lost control of his sons, their hatred undermined his family. Marduk, along with his son, Nabu, sought to steal power away from his own brothers. Nergal, who was unwilling to give Marduk all the power, put up the biggest fight, even forming an alliance with Enlil's son, Ninurta.

Ninurta commanded the Enlilite flight squadrons which patrolled Terra. He had led the famed Gutian Hordes into Akkad to destroy what was left of my armies, and Ninurta was given the task of restoring the water systems of the Euphrates after Marduk had contaminated them.

Ninurta and his wife, Gula, were stationed in the city of Lagash. Ninurta, who loved flying and commanding the air force, was also fond of building and engineering; he looked forward to the challenge of cleaning up the river. But he detested the daily grind of governing and had no patience for the social life that accompanied such duties. His wife, Gula, was devoted to him, but alas, Ninurta was too strange to be anyone's companion. Perhaps he had built a wall around himself to deflect the constant attentions of his overbearing mother, Ninhursag.

Ninurta became more remote, withdrawing into himself. He neglected the governing of the cities and disappeared for days, flying off in his favorite air ship, the Black Bird.

Ninurta wanted to build pyramids. Ever since the war, he had been envious of the great pyramids of Egypt, and he invited the Egyptian architects who had been a part of the design and building in Giza to begin work in Sumer. To his wife's pleasure, this occupied him for a time, keeping him near home. But gradually the lure of flying alone in his ship called to him. Flying far from all civilization, Ninurta wandered endlessly through remote mountains. He formed a legion of fighters in these mountains and taught them the martial arts, enjoying the simple company of these rustic men.

Ninurta became disillusioned with the ways of his family, the gods. Troubled in his heart by our endless conflicts, he reflected back on his childhood when Terra was an unknown adventure. He longed for the time when he had been free from the ominous responsibilities of being Enlil's son. I will freely admit that I've never completely understood Ninurta. He is a complex person always torn between the burden of his duties and a compelling need to simply be a playful little boy, the little boy he had perhaps never been.

With Ninurta out of the way for long periods of time, Marduk looked back at his Babylon and the surrounding cities. He and his followers began to infiltrate villages of the neighboring countryside and, using holography, Marduk appeared before the leaders of certain tribes, calling himself by many names. These tribes were encouraged to bow down and worship Lord Marduk. He performed many miracles for them, gave them power and wealth, and warned them that the gods of Enlil and his kind were false gods. Marduk told the tribespeople that those who did not worship him would be punished; they would be damned to a hell forever.

The humans had been conditioned over the centuries to worship something outside themselves, namely *us*; and they had very little defense against such manipulation. How were they to know which god was true? Certainly, all of the gods were fickle, they had abandoned the humans more than once. The tribespeople reasoned perhaps they should follow the god who provided for them best; or might it be better to obey the god who threatened terrible punishments, just to avoid such things?

Marduk did an excellent job of confusing people. By insidiously eroding the power of the other gods, he began to win the devotion of the Lulus. The science of mind control and brainwashing propaganda was in its beginning stages.

In Ninurta's absence, Enlil realized he must appoint someone better suited to the task of ruling Sumer. He chose my father, Nannar. From the city of Ur, Nannar and Ningal, my mother, began to rebuild the normal trade routes and to restore agriculture and business in the area. The temples resumed their normal activities and new ziggurats were constructed.

Yet, things were not right. There was friction and enmity in the very air of Terra. It was as if the planet were a being who could not bear the struggles and hatreds of the gods, and an uneasy feeling surrounded all. Ambition and greed ran rampant throughout the land; one kingship was declared only to be overthrown by another. Skirmishes increased as tempers flared. The eyes of Marduk glanced out over his future domains.

You can read the history of this time for yourself, as much was written in the clay tablets. Marduk and his son, Nabu, battled and warred with the Enlilites over and over to gain territory and control of the Spaceport. On the side of Enlil were my father, Nannar, my brother, Utu, Ninurta, and Nergal, the son of Enki.

Toward the end of these terrible wars, Matali went to his old friend, Enki. Matali had always been in command of Enki's personal ship and the two had passed many an hour together. Matali begged Enki to speak to his sons. What was to be gained by this endless fighting? Surely the land and people of Terra would only suffer more. What if the sons of Enki and Enlil were to die in battle? What would be left for either of the patriarchs? The outcome of this war could only be mutual annihilation, as both sides had awesome weapons. If Anu called for the Gandiva, no one could stop it. Who could predict the end of such a devastating war?

After listening to Matali, Enki visited his son, Nergal, and tried to reason with him. But Nergal resisted; he had always believed that Enki favored Marduk. The truth was more pathetic. Marduk possessed a subtle form of mind control over his father, and Enki was simply powerless in Marduk's presence. Nergal was only further enraged by Enki's attempts to coerce him into making peace with Marduk. The angry Nergal ordered Enki to leave, and cursed both his father and brother, vowing to destroy them!

Alone, poor Enki sadly wept. He did not know what to

do and he longed for happier times, even for Antu's parties!

The prophets of doom began to multiply. Across the land, every priest and soothsayer whispered tales of ensuing destruction, and the end of the world was prophesied by oracles in all of the temples. Many of the predictions were absurd and never came true, but it was as if people were addicted to such pronouncements. The more frightening and ghastly the forecasts, the more money people would pay to hear them. The prophets were indeed making great profits!

New buildings were erected to hold all the Lulus who desired to gather and be filled with fear. Tales of the coming famines and the devastation of entire cities were among the most popular prophecies, while earthquakes and floods tied for second place. The Lulus would pay all their money to come and listen to such tales, to be frightened out of their wits. This fear generated an energy which Marduk learned to *feed* off of, and he began to encourage fear by projecting holographic images onto the skies, creating terrifying visionary scenes. He experimented with this fear energy, manipulating and modifying it to satiate his appetite. It was better than human flesh, and easier to manage.

The prophecies became self-fulfilling. One dreadful day, the armies of Marduk swept down upon Enlil's holy city, Nippur. Ninurta rallied his troops in defense, but the temple and holy shrines were destroyed. An implacable Enlil responded by mandating the destruction of Babylon, the city most beloved by Marduk, along with all of Marduk's logistical centers.

Enlil called a Council of War and the dreaded question was put to his father, Anu. The Gandiva weapon could only be activated by the command of Anu, for once the great Gandiva was unleashed, the outcome could not be predicted.

Nergal attempted one last meeting with his brother, Marduk. If Marduk would give up his claims to supreme rulership, the Gandiva would remain sleeping. Enki, who was present with Marduk and Nabu, seemed to be in a state of blindness, as if his will had been broken. Engulfed in darkness, Enki spewed out his rage and frustration at Nergal, and Nergal's anger grew. Leaving his father and Marduk, Nergal determined to use the Gandiva. Nothing could stop it now.

All the gods were aware of the possible dangers of the Gandiva. Even Marduk became afraid when he realized that his brother, Nergal, really meant to use it.

Anu was filled with sorrow. The jealousy of his sons had brought Terra to this. Anu could see how weak his son, Enki, had become, and Anu preferred to destroy the cities and the Spaceport rather than allow everything to fall into the hands of the unruly Marduk. Anu and Enlil saw something dark, almost evil, in Marduk and his ambitions. Marduk wanted to take over the entire planet Terra, to take power from Anu, and even to rule the Pleiades. Marduk had become a serious threat, like a machine devouring everything in its way, with no feeling, no heart, no joy of *being*, only in ruthless conquest.

Anu unleashed the Gandiva. A blaze of light, razor sharp and more potent than the sun, flashed in a zigzagging motion. Although aimed at specific objectives, the doomsday weapon was impervious to distinctions.

It was not just the Spaceport that was destroyed; many other locations logistically important to Marduk on Terra disappeared as well. The entire Sinai Peninsula was laid to waste, along with numerous other targets. But what became crucial was something we had not planned for and could not control: the wind.

It is an irony that the name Enlil can mean "Lord of the Wind," but in that moment, neither Enlil nor any other god could control the winds of death that blew over Sumer. Clouds of radiation swept across the plains, killing every human and animal in their path. The radiation poisoning disintegrated the cells of their bodies, the skin fell from their bones, their blood evaporated in the dry scorching winds, and they died in agonizing pain. The ones on the periphery suffered the most horribly; it took them the longest to die. The lands were black with nuclear fires, and the waters were contaminated with poison.

Safe in their ships, the gods watched as once again their folly destroyed millions of lives. Entire villages vanished in total annihilation; animals and crops, bridges and ziggurats disappeared from the face of the planet as Terra herself convulsed in pain.

What had they done? Only a few survivors remained amidst the dreadful devastation that once had been a green and beautiful planet. The violence of the Gandiva and the ensuing radiation clouds created a shock, and this shock became a wave which sent a signal out into the solar system.

Moving past the last planets of the Sun, the signal traveled across the galaxy and on past, further out into other sectors. Across the vastness of space, this signal was received by the Council of the Intergalactic Federation. Those Pleiadians playing around on the planet Earth had finally gone too far. They must be stopped. Such irresponsible behavior could not and would not be tolerated. The equilibrium of the entire Universe had been disturbed.

A call went out, and we were summoned to the Great Hall of the Intergalactic Federation Council.

We had been so immersed in ourselves and our play, that we had forgotten all about the rest of the Universe. Who were these intruders who dared call us from our play? Anu knew very well who they were, and he summoned us all with authority.

# XVI

# INTERFERENCE

The Great Hall of the Intergalatic Federation Council was an immense meeting room with high, vaulted, transparent ceilings that looked out on infinite space. Anu, Enlil, Enki, Ninhursag, Nannar, Ninurta, Nergal, Utu, and I were all formally seated in the circle of the Council. Marduk refused to attend. I suddenly felt small, and was glad Anu was there; but even he seemed diminished in these surroundings. The very presence of the Council members made us humble, a feeling we were not accustomed to.

The twelve Overseers of the Council represented a cross-section of the galaxies. In the audience were hundreds of other representatives from all across the Universe. So many species! Members were present from Sirius, Andromeda, Orion, Arcturus, and countless other star systems.

The Etherians were noticeably present. Etherians have

a very high vibrational frequency. At times they appear solid, at other times transparent or translucent, and it is said that they are beyond polarity, although I have yet to experience such a state. I didn't know why, but the Etherians appeared to have the last word in conducting the meeting.

I also saw beings that were spheres or balls of light that flew around you, changing into all the colors of the spectrum; first golden, then rose or turquoise. They possessed the peculiar ability to enter into you with your permission, to fill your cells with light and through this, know the sum total of your being. I found this to be a most interesting way of communicating. I was having fun with all these new experiences when the mood in the Hall shifted.

As Anu stood to face the Twelve, a sound came from them simultaneously. This sound became words which were clearly understood by each race: "NO INTERFERENCE!"

*No interference* is the law of this free-will Universe, and we, the Twelve said, had violated the law by directly interfering with the evolution of a species. The law stated it was permissible to assist in the evolution of beings if, and only if, they requested such assistance. To tamper with their DNA and disrupt the electromagnetic fields of an entire planet with the Gandiva weapon was unconscionable and illegal.

I thought, to myself, that this free-will Universe concept must be like free trade on Terra; it is only free when it suits those who are in power. It looked to me as if this Council was trying to exert power over us by interfering with *our* free will.

It was obvious to the Council that we did not yet fully understand, so they carefully explained to us that no one was going to punish us, blow us up, or take our toys away. Something would happen to us, however. A state of consciousness, an energy, a mood which reflected the sum total of all our actions on Terra would find its way into our world. This energy would slowly but surely choke the creativity and spontaneity out of our lives, and we would find ourselves blocked, unable to evolve. The Council called this energy *The Wall*. They stated very clearly that we were not victims, that we had created this *Wall* ourselves; it was the child of our own making. We did not believe them.

They also forbade us to ever use the Gandiva again. If we did so, it would be viewed as an act of war and we would be dealt with summarily. If we did not believe that their weapons were more powerful than ours, perhaps we could be shown some holographic memoirs of other errant groups who had been annihilated for breaking the law. It was further explained that their weapons not only destroyed civilizations, they were also powerful enough to vaporize the souls of the inhabitants. We could all be returned back into the mind of Prime Creator to be no more, with no more incarnations available to us in any form! A cold chill ran up my pretty blue neck.

The Council went on to say that later in our development it would be obvious to us that we had been in an adolescent phase. Such rivalries as those between Enki and Enlil would eventually pass, having served their natural purpose. In the meantime, we would not be allowed to destroy planets and fracture time itself with these high-energy explosions. Remember. They concluded with the word REMEMBER!!!

Anu was visibly stunned. I had never seen him like this. As I tried to get his attention, he barely noticed me. Anu returned to Nibiru, Enki and Enlil flew to the orbiting space station, and the three stayed in constant communication.

Amid all the discussion and arguments, with each son blaming the other, an urgent message appeared on our communication screens. Marduk had laid siege to the entire Pleiadian star system. For many years Marduk had secretly cloned and trained legions of armies on an abandoned planet. The fear he had learned to extricate from the human race was serving as food and energy to support this massive effort. In a surprise attack, he had maneuvered into the Pleiades and destroyed the ruling dynasty there. Now in complete tyrannical control, Marduk ordered Anu to surrender, or he would destroy Nibiru. Anu escaped with Antu to a neighboring star system.

We were all in shock. Enki and I flew to Inner Earth with Matali to hide in the deep underground world of the Snake Kingdom, where we would be protected from any residue of the Gandiva's radiation. Enlil left to join his father, Anu. The two were determined to formulate a plan to regain Nibiru and free the Pleiades.

Safely beyond the time frequencies of the damaged planet, our family watched in horror as Marduk began to take over what was left of Terra and her inhabitants. Over time, he seized control of your planet. Marduk did not use armies to conquer Terra; instead, he used propaganda. The priests of Marduk accused Enlil of unleashing the terrible Gandiva against the helpless humans. It was, after all, the truth, and thus Marduk turned Terra's inhabitants against Anu and Enlil.

Marduk went out of his way to slander me. He claimed I was an evil witch who devoured men and turned innocent women into whores. Coveting my temples and all the lands owned by my priestesses, Marduk embarked on a campaign to slander and destroy these women. My priestesses, who were highly trained in business and the arts, were accused of black magic, of casting dark spells over the land. Whenever anything went wrong, if there was a bad storm or a crop failure, my women were blamed. And Marduk saw to it that plenty went wrong. My beautiful priestesses were imprisoned, beaten, tortured, raped, and burned alive. All of their property was confiscated. Marduk was taking his revenge on me, the one who had ordered him buried alive.

In the Snake Kingdom, I lay on a small bed in a lovely room, but I did not notice my surroundings. In the Eye of my Mind, I saw my temples defaced and mutilated by Marduk's men. All images of the goddess were replaced with his own. He carved his name in stone over mine and rewrote history, making himself the hero of every story and legend. I watched in helpless agony as my priestesses suffered every imaginable humiliation. There are many so-called fairy tales of virgin girls taken by dragons and chained in dark caverns. These stories are based on truth, but there was no knight in shining armor to rescue my beautiful priestesses.

Marduk did not stop with my women; he would not be satisfied until he had suppressed *all* women. To achieve this, he used the men. He told the human males that they were superior, that woman was created from the rib of man to serve him. Lies, lies poured forth from the priests of Marduk.

As women lost their place of respect, the men in turn lost a part of themselves. Nothing was ever right again. Even lovemaking became a war. Because Marduk wanted more subjects to control and more energy from the fear being generated, he encouraged his subjects to procreate. He placed an electromagnetic device in Terra's moon which tied female ovulation to its cycles. The animals of Terra cannot be impregnated so frequently as its women. Marduk wanted to produce fear as a commodity, so he ordered the Lulus to multiply themselves, giving him more subjects to tyrannize, and so that he could generate energy from their fear.

Fear became the commodity most valued by Marduk. Fear ruled: fear of death, fear of punishment, and fear of knowledge. With such an unlimited source, Marduk could feed his legions of clones, and Terra became a power station for Marduk and his tyrants.

And tyrants there were; from the rulers of countries to the heads of companies, tyranny was the law. To exert one's will over another was the most highly valued expression of human life. With tyranny came its friend, greed, and as no one can be close to those they control, things, the trophies of conquest and control, took the place of love. Pleasure was defined by possessions, and things took the place of intimacy.

From the Snake Kingdom, I saw this world's future time line unfold before me. I saw Marduk becoming more and more clever in his techniques to control the Lulus and generate fear. Priests and politicians paraded before me; styles changed, but the underlying tyranny remained the same. An invisible claw spread over the minds and souls of the inhabitants of Terra. The Inquisition, the feudal system, a hundred 'isms' all promising hope came and left. Industrialization brought meaningless labor, increased materialism, and contaminated the waters, the land, and the food.

Marduk perfected manipulation with the advent of mass media—television and journalism. Over and over the humans were entrained to worship outside themselves, never encouraged to turn inward. There was always someone out there to be worshipped, someone better and higher. Doubting themselves, the Lulus listened endlessly to the "experts," who in turn contradicted each other, adding further to the confusion.

The humans who did manage to think for themselves were ostracized as misfits, punished, or at the very least made to feel guilty. If one accomplished, others felt diminished, and guilt was encouraged. Psychology became popular, and humans gave their money to those who would listen to their guilt and fear for hours, days, years. For Marduk, guilt was just as nourishing as fear.

If there was a shortage of fear, Marduk would throw in a famine, an earthquake, or a hurricane. This could be real, actually occurring in Nature, or it might be simply shown as a hologram or on the television.

From my little bed, the future of Terra looked abysmal.

As I wandered back and forth through time, it suddenly dawned on me like lightning striking my poor tired brain that Marduk was us! Marduk was the collective unconscious of the family of Anu projected out onto Terra. We had created him as surely as we had ever done anything in our lives. Each and every one of us had borne Marduk into this dimension. Surely, if we had created him, we could also get rid of him. But how?

# XVII

# DESCENT

I went to my friends, Matali and Tara, and told them that I desired to return to the Old Serpent Woman. Tara led me to her caverns. The Old Serpent Woman did not seem surprised to see me, and though she spoke no words, I understood that I must go alone on a journey.

The wise lady led me down a long dark tunnel, and at its end I saw a transparent oval, like a womb surrounded by a translucent shell of soft flowing light. I stepped inside and sat down for what seemed like an eternity. Nothing happened. I began to perform austerities, disciplines to raise my frequencies through focus. I breathed; I created tapas, divine heat; I fasted; I stood motionless on one toe for 2,000 years; I prostrated myself; I wept. My soul poured itself out into that oval as silence pressed itself in on me.

Yet nothing happened. I looked at my life as Inanna.

Everything I had ever been or done moved across the Eye of my Mind. The longing for truth and understanding overwhelmed my very being, and my lovely body heaved and shook in sobbing and despair. At last, I gave up despair and lost myself in the heat of fire, as I sacrificed my pride and no longer knew who I was. The *I* of Inanna faded away.

As all identity fell from my being like the tears from my eyes, a light began to form in front of me. Slowly, this light formed into the most exquisitely beautiful being I had ever seen. It was neither man nor woman, but its form was human. It was made up of myriads of tiny lights shooting, moving constantly in ever-changing colors. The face was a face of a thousand beings, and it radiated all I could hope to be: love, grace, wisdom, and qualities that have no words to describe them.

"What is your name?" I asked.

Answering me, the Being spoke thus:

"I have many names from a multitude of experiences and states of being, but my true spirit wherein my soul resides is only a light frequency, not a name. I am that which cannot be named. If you seek to name me, say I am Altair from Alcyone, Star from Star. I am that which you have always been.

"Your longing for truth has brought me here. These are the moments of your awakening; treasure them. Unfoldment is taking place now within this timescape. You are a response system. I interface with you. I have been aligning your circuitry for better reception. Attune to me.

"Remember, beloved. Remember your true Home. When Time began for you, you were a pure white light. Now you have many colors, many nuances, many experiences. You float through a Sea of Timelessness, pulsating Beauty. I love you greatly."

I felt my body being caressed by a soft gentle breeze. The immense love of this being wrapped itself around me, healing me and drying my tears. I felt lighter and waves of sheer joy ran through me.

The Being spoke again:

"I love you, Inanna.

I NEVER judged you.

I rejoiced at your accomplishments, at your courage.

I wept when you wept.

I sought wisdom in your beauty.

I held you in your darkest hours.

I was never separate from you. I allowed you
    to move in the ways you chose in order to
    bring me experience.

Would any being do less for its child, its creation?

In the sweetness of our coming together, I open
    myself to you.

I hasten to you to fill myself in you and of you.

You are my creation and I have longed for
    your Return.

Not demanding, you turn to me,

Gently, as the flowers following the sun.

Your being creates a space for me to fill.

Oh, My Beloved! United we are!

From all the pathways and trails,

Through the long and lonely corridors of Time,

As the streams of the Earth,

As the blood flowing in your veins,

We meet in the Heart.

There to burn in the Fires of Our Becoming."

It was so! I was on fire! My entire being was burning with Love and I experienced an ecstasy I had never before imagined. In silence, the Being conveyed to my mind an understanding. Love welled up inside me with an indescribable force of passion. In my heart I knew what I would do. The heat of fire forever changed me.

I saw my future. I would descend into human form, become human, and attempt to activate the divine gene in my selves. I would separate myself in varying portions and take many incarnations. I would dare to make myself vulnerable and be born into human flesh. I chose a wide variety of experiences through particular bloodlines. Even though I would descend into Earth time, I knew this Being of Light would always be with me, and I would never be truly alone again.

At first, I admit I was a little reticent about actually getting into human flesh. I knew exactly what had been done to human DNA and how difficult it would be to remember who I was, once in. But I was determined.

I decided to begin slowly. In the Himalayan mountains, there lived a group of humans who had banded together in search of wisdom. By praying and meditating, they were hoping for a vision which might bring them truth. As an experiment, I generated a holographic image of myself, slightly modified, and I appeared to them. Wearing white robes, I surrounded myself with a modest amount of light and focused on the thought of Love shown to me by the great being in the Oval. I pictured a column of light coming from the Oval, flowing through me, out onto the mountains, and into the hearts and minds of these seekers.

Their innocence and gratitude caused me to love them, and the more I loved, the more solid I became. I was a little afraid, but I could not help loving them. Their joy was a sweetness I had never known. As my physical density increased, I knew that soon I might forget, that I might not remember who I was or why I had come here. I thought of all the others I would become. The force of my loving and compassion set into motion one hundred lives, as I, Inanna, disguised as a Lulu, descended onto Terra to experience all the limitations of flesh and blood.

I had hoped to find this task an easy one, an adventure. After all, I as Inanna was from a different time frequency and I was used to time traveling. How difficult could it be? My optimism was, however, misplaced. The density of Terra's vibrational frequencies combined with a body whose deactivated DNA allowed only one-tenth of its brain to function left me overwhelmed by the five senses, and confusion and fear repetitiously set in. In lifetime after lifetime, Marduk's brainwashing techniques, propaganda, and frequency control proved too much for me. The current belief system would simply overwhelm me and I became lost.

As a man, I chose the life of a priest in Atlantis. I was keeper of the sacred crystals. I fell in love with a holy virgin, defiled her, and was executed by my peers. In ancient Ireland, I became a powerful warrior. Wielding my axe, I chopped the heads off a thousand men and stacked them in front of my castle as a display of my wealth. Indulging in drink, I beat my wife. Persuading my son to slit my throat as I slept, my wife and my brother stole my life and my wealth. In Egypt, I became the librarian of the great store of scrolls and clay tablets at Alexandria. Fearful of all feeling, I lived alone amongst the written word. A rigid and lonely old man, I died in the great fire when Roman soldiers burned down the library.

As a woman, I became a dancer in Kashmir to honor my friend Tara. An orphan who danced her way into the palace, I determined to educate myself by learning languages and architecture. I was much admired by men, but the women in the harem despised me and soon poisoned me. In western America, I became an Indian girl, riding ponies and hunting on the plains. My name was Sky Maiden, and communing with the stars, I blessed Earth with the energies of the heavens. In love with a handsome brave, Flame Feather, I died in childbirth tied to the floor of my tepee by a superstitious medicine man. In Spain, I became a lovely young Jewish girl. Thrown in prison during the Inquisition, I was tortured and burned alive at the stake. Before I died, beautiful angels came to me to release me from my body and the pain.

I became many. I experienced life as a man and as a woman. I walked the same roads humans have walked. I felt what they have felt, the same hope and despair. I held a child in my arms; I was a child with no mother. I slaughtered many men and loved many. I wondered bitterly, what did it matter? What did anything matter?

Praying for help, I sat on the cold ground and gazed longingly up at the stars. I tried to remember.

# XVIII

# FOR THE CHILDREN

Ninhursag joined her brother, Enki, in the Snake Kingdom and they watched me in my human incarnations with a keen interest. Ninhursag and Enki had created the human species so long ago and knew the possibility of activating their "divine" genes in spite of the veil of Marduk's control. My great-aunt Nin was excited by the unlimited potential lying dormant within every human. She had always loved her Lulus. Enki had saved the Lulus from total annihilation after the Flood, and he wanted the chance to help them again. Besides, the challenge of such an adventure was intriguing to him. So Enki and Ninhursag joined me in my descent into human flesh and blood.

We all knew the dangers that lay ahead of us. We might never remember who we were; we might get lost. We took a vow to help each other *remember* whenever and however possible. Other gods followed our course. My mother, Ningal, and my father, Nannar, were joined by my twin brother, Utu, and his lovely wife. Ninurta followed his mother, Ninhursag, wanting to protect her. Even my half-sister, Ereshkigal, and her husband, Nergal, chose to incarnate as humans. Many others followed into their own bloodlines, incarnating into the lineages they had created and were already a part of.

As for their experiences, you'll have to ask them. Perhaps they are you.

The Intergalactic Council was very impressed by our fearless commitment to remove *The Wall*. Boredom can be quite a motivation. A new message from the Council went out into the Universe concerning the planet Terra. A special version was transmitted to Marduk and his followers.

*No one outside Terra's frequencies was to interfere with her.* She was to be left alone, allowed to evolve on her own, until the end of the year 2011 AD. Terra would be protected by a battalion of ships from all across the galaxies sponsored by the Council.

In the year 2012 AD, this agreement would be terminated. At that time, Terra would experience a dimensional split and separate herself into two distinct dimensions. In the Universe when disputes could not be settled peacefully, such conflicts were often resolved by dimensional separations. Time and physical reality are much like the layers of an onion. Worlds can and do exist within worlds, and dimensional existences overlap and intertwine one another.

This separation would barely be noticed by the inhabitants of Terra, and all would be given plenty of time to choose between the two dimensions. The individual nature of each human would determine this choice; no one would choose for anyone else.

One Terra would contain the frequencies of the so-called Light and would exist in what is termed a fourth dimension. In the fourth dimension, whatever thoughts an individual might have would become real as each thought instantly manifested itself, and all would come to know that they themselves create their own reality. All of the inhabitants of this Terra would know that they alone were responsible for everything they experienced, and the inherent right to be sovereign and to create would be guaranteed to everyone.

The other Terra would belong to Marduk and his tyrants. Those who wanted to be told what to do, how to think, and not to exercise choice in their lives would remain under the control of Marduk. Beings could go on experiencing life under the aegis of his rules as tyranny continued to reign and Marduk was allowed to have his creation. There were, it seemed, many who remained content to have someone else think for them, and many who preferred to worship something forever outside of themselves.

There would be no judgment as Terra became two distinct worlds. One day all humans would simply find themselves in the dimension which suited them best, barely noticing any change at all, although there might remain some vague memories, even a few myths about a distant past.

In the interim, the Council and the Etherians would stand as guardians over Terra. There would be no wars; no conquests from space would be permitted. Apparently there were many other civilizations from other sectors who also wanted Terra. Many asserted they had also seeded her in eons past, and were returning to renew their claims. This small blue planet seems to be highly valued by many. Surely there must be something on Terra greater than gold.

In a way, we all cheated just a little. We *did* interfere. We entered human bodies attempting to activate the "divine" gene. We wanted to encourage original thinking and foment rebellion against tyranny. However, this proved to be hard going, and we were frequently executed for such behavior in one gruesome manner or another. We succeeded in creating a few inspiring holograms, some uplifting visions and other "holy" experiences. And we did give some technological tips to a few of your best thinkers along the way.

Naturally, Marduk also cheated. In trying to win converts, he generated many fearful holograms. He specialized in separating religion from the rest of life, and he created many forms of worship with vast bureaucracies to tax and rule the Lulus. He created a new religion which had no official name but was known to some as *consumerism*. Men and women came to regard things as more important than people, and people were measured by the number and quantity of their things.

An altar, an electronic box that emitted pictures, was installed in every house to train people to worship things and to acquire more of them. This altar consumed most of people's time. The remainder of their time was spent in getting money to buy things. Children were left alone in front of the altar while their parents rushed about in the pursuit of more things. Only a few noticed how empty life had become. Marduk had succeeded in painting a new face on his old snake oil, over and over.

When the Etherians heard about the altar, they

resolved to send the people of Terra a gift. From the center of the galaxy, they began to transmit a *Wave* of light. Gently at first, then slowly increasing in magnitude, *The Wave* surrounded Terra. New generations of thought appeared for no reason, often befuddling confused parents. People danced in the streets like primitive tribes shouting "make love, not war!" Many others found themselves seeking solitude, time to go inside themselves.

*The Wave* continued. Grown men declared their right to feel, and women asserted that they were equal to men. Young students stood in front of enormous weapons and claimed their right to choose, to be free. People rallied to defend Mother Earth, who had been poisoned terribly in the twentieth century. Some claimed to speak with the dolphins and other animals, wanting to defend them.

*The Wave* grows more powerful. I, Inanna, seemingly lost here in a strange earthly body, open myself to that Wave. Every day, I endeavor to remember.

Somewhere in time, I see a little blue girl running across a lapis floor, and her laughter echoes in my memory. I know I must remember. If I can remember, surely all of us can. Surely remembering and awakening will spread like a wildfire through the very air we all breathe. I open myself to *The Wave*.

Some days I am confused, but this remembering grows steadily within me. There is a vision of a Being of Light who loves me, and I can feel that Love. There are Spheres of Light that sometimes fly around me. *The Wave* grows stronger. I hear the sounds of change. Every cell of my body begins to vibrate with change as endless sweet mysteries reveal themselves to me.

I remember...I remember...The gentle waves of Love and forgiveness flow across my body, into my mind, into my heart, and I *remember*.

So, we are here on Terra with you, awaiting the time of choice. We who created you send our Love to all our many children. We who created Marduk want you to become as the "gods," but better! We want you to take back what we stole from you in eons past; your power, the power to trust in yourselves. *The Wave* is for every human on this plane. *The Wave* is our Love for you, our children.

We come in the night in your dreams, in the singing of birds, the caress of the wind, the rustling of leaves, the scent of flowers, a baby's laugh. We follow you down the corridors of Time and whisper in your hearts, "Beloved, wake up! Know who you are." And most of all, we send you Love, for Love is the greatest power of all.

As you begin to discover your power to create, occasionally think of me and my folly. Think of Ninhursag and Enki, all of us. Remember our story, and have as much fun as we do!

As for me, I saw the most intriguing and interesting man at the Intergalactic Council. I have never seen a man like him, and after I get past this *Wall* thing, I think I will look for him. Perhaps he will notice me now. I have changed. Perhaps I will find him in the Etherian Bar on the Seventh Bardo Plane. Perhaps life is just beginning for me, Inanna.

*End of Part I*

# INTERIM

A beautiful woman, a goddess, sleeps upon a golden dragon.

The dragon hisses, eyes glowing red in the darkness.

The woman lies under a thick velvet cover, her arms languid, her delicate fingers still and silent. Her skin is creamy blue, warm and soft. Her almond-shaped eyes move imperceptibly behind closed lids and long eyelashes.

She sleeps. She dreams...

Seated on a cloud, she hovers in the sky as thousands of men and women prostrate themselves before her in worship and adoration.

Inanna! They cry!

Oh! Queen of Heaven! They cry! We bow before you!

Suddenly, from beneath her, venomous snakes appear.

Writhing from her, they crawl toward the crowds.

First snakes, then dragons, then demons.

They devour her worshippers.

Terror fills the air. Blood stains the land.

No! The goddess screams. No!

I am you. Do not worship me! No!

Her anguish overcomes her. Gasping for breath, she wakens, trembling and crying. No! Tiny beads of sweat cover her body. No! Tears flow across her lovely face.

The dragon hisses...and then is silent once more.

I

# THE RED SHOES

The year is 1994, the location: Planet Earth, New York City, the upper west side. Gracie gets out of a taxi on Broadway and 78th Street clutching a shopping bag from an expensive mid-town department store firmly in her arms. Exhilarated and nervous at the same time, she ponders her state of mind. She has just paid almost $300.00 for a pair of red high heels, an obscene amount, she knows, to pay for a pair of shoes. After years of meditating and seeking truth, traveling all over the world and looking for answers in thousands of books, here she is standing on the mean streets of New York City gripping a pair of red high-heeled shoes which cost enough to feed a family of six for a year in some Third-World country.

A loudly moaning voice enters Gracie's awareness. She turns to see a young woman slouched over on concrete steps. She is shabbily dressed, dirty, and visibly distraught; her face is bruised. Weeping hysterically, the young woman cries out in a loud voice, "I have nothing! Nowhere to live! Nothing to feed my children!" Her desperation fills the street as she begs passersby for anything. Being in New York City, they naturally ignore her completely.

The shopping bag grows heavier in Gracie's arms. Feeling faint and guilty, she discreetly opens her purse and pulls out twenty dollars, careful not to attract any attention from potential muggers. Slowly walking toward the sad young woman, Gracie drops the twenty-dollar bill into calloused, waiting hands.

Screaming at the top of her powerful lungs, the woman jumps to her feet. "TWENTY DOLLARS!!! My God! This woman gave me twenty dollars!!!" Every person within hearing range stops and turns to look at Gracie and the woman. Gracie knows that if she remains there for one more minute, she will be mobbed by desperate souls begging her for more money. In sheer panic, Gracie begins to run, dodging traffic as she races across Broadway on 78th Street and down to Riverside Drive. Kissing the doorman as she enters her apartment building, she hurries to the elevator and sags against its comforting walls, her heart beating loudly.

The shoes are gone.

In another dimension, Inanna, the beautiful Pleiadian goddess, sits in a transparent oval contemplating the multi-dimensional selves she has projected out onto the time/space continuum. An impulse of fear and panic from one of the selves reaches her. Focusing on the area of irritation, Inanna pulls up the image of Gracie in the elevator. The girl's heart is racing dangerously; perhaps a little soothing is necessary.

Gracie hears a familiar voice in her mind. "Calm down, you're all right. It was nice of you to help that poor woman. Breathe deeply and calm yourself." Gracie begins to cry as she opens the door of her apartment. Two wonderful black German Shepherds jump all over Gracie, kissing her tears and welcoming her home. She gratefully embraces her guardian angels.

Gracie moves to the window. After twenty years in New York City, she is finally living in an apartment with a stunning view of the Hudson River. The apartment is on the twentieth floor, maybe one floor for every year. From the safety of her perch, Gracie looks down to Riverside Park. It is spring and the cherry blossoms are in full bloom. The beauty is deceiving, shrouding the cardboard boxes hidden behind trees and shrubs, the homes of so many homeless. From this view, she can clearly see them. "I can't take it anymore. I can't bear to feel so helpless against such overwhelming despair!" She remembers the man who lives in the park all winter, covering himself with newspapers to keep warm. In mutual fear, their eyes have met more than once. His eyes expressed his isolation and pain, penetrated the depths of her soul and left her feeling utterly helpless.

The pain of the city is more than she can witness. Gracie dreams of mountains in the Pacific Northwest, of cedar forests and clean water. Hugging her dogs, she vows to pack up and leave the city, which for her has become an empty promise.

✸

Inanna relaxes, knowing that Gracie has received the images of the mountain sanctuary and taken them deep into her being. Soon Gracie will be alone on Lost Mountain with only the stars. Without the chaos of the city, she might listen to Inanna, and in the silence of the forest, Gracie may remember. Perhaps this one will do better than the others. Perhaps this one will activate the recessive genes and be able to collect the other selves who are lost in their belief systems. Perhaps this young woman will succeed where the others have failed.

# II

# THE BRILLIANTS

Inanna gazed down at her blue skin. Noting the pale exhausted tone of her skin cells, she decided to rest for awhile. Inanna contemplated her multidimensional selves, wondering why she could not break through to them. Only last week Olnwynn was murdered by his very own son. When Inanna decided to incarnate into a variety of human beings, she had no idea that life in a human body could be so confusing and dangerous. There was something so dense about the whole experience; no wonder the human race was having such a difficult time of it. And the advent of the Kali Yuga had only exacerbated matters.

Pleiadian civilization has always understood that the phases of creation continually take place in four cycles known as the ages or Yugas. The first period is a golden age where wisdom and accomplishment are the rule. This phase is followed by a second age in which wisdom is replaced by ritual. The third cycle is an age of doubt; Prime Creator loses Itself in Its creation, and man and woman forget their divine origin. Finally comes the fourth age, the Kali Yuga, which can be described as an age of darkness, confusion, and conflict; all the values of the first golden age are reversed. The inferior mind rules as greed and fear prevail.

In the suffocating atmosphere of this Kali Yuga, Inanna's cousin Marduk and his lieutenants had cranked up the limiting *extremely low frequency* electromagnetic fields, the ELFs, to further confuse and bewilder Earth's inhabitants. Surrounded by a virtual prison of electromagnetic waves, people were no longer able to be still and listen to their *inner* hearts. Rushing to nowhere, they worried, paid bills, borrowed more, and sat endlessly in front of their televisions waiting for someone to give them answers. People accumulated possessions, believing their things would keep them safe from harm. The idea of the end of the world was becoming more and more popular. Chaos and confusion increased daily.

In her growing frustration, Inanna hissed with her guardian dragons. The more impossible it seemed, the more determined she became to help liberate the human species. Lying down to close her eyes, Inanna allowed her mind to drift and forced herself to relax, forgetting about her multi-dimensional selves for a moment. A cool breeze floated across her lovely body as she thought of her home planet, Nibiru, and of the wonderful parties her great-grandmother used to give. She saw herself as a small child stuffing exotic chocolates from Valthezon into her mouth. She tasted the memory; a sweet liquid filled her mouth and dribbled down her chin. She giggled.

"Inanna!" a voice called to her. It was a familiar voice,

but she could not quite place it. It was not any of her Earth selves, nor was it one of her notorious family. "Inanna! Don't you remember, before you were born into the family of Anu? Remember a time before you were born into your lovely blue body, before Nibiru and Earth."

Inanna furrowed her perfect eyebrows. Her thoughts formed in her mind. "You mean before I became me, Inanna? What could I have been before me?"

A vision came before the Eye of her Mind: an infinite number of colored geometric light forms constantly changed in rapid succession. She endeavored to make the forms stay still so that she could identify even one of them, but they refused to do so. "Inanna, it is me, your old mentor, Melinar!"

*Melinar!* The name was so familiar to Inanna. She stretched her consciousness. There had been another sort of experience. Shadowy memories moved into her thoughts. Melinar! My teacher! Now *here* was a time frequency. If Earth time could be described as dense, sticky taffy, the dimension of Melinar was vapor and mist.

Inanna pursued the vision with her focus. Occasionally the form of a face would momentarily appear, only to disappear again. The face was familiar, gentle and kind, an old man with sparkling green eyes that reminded Inanna of her favorite emeralds. Then she remembered why she loved jewelry; the rapidly changing vision Melinar presented was like thousands of mutating cut stones shining with transparent inner light. She had once been just this form and she remembered it quite clearly. She had once been a body of 144 geometric forms in perpetual motion known as the brilliants.

One day she had become tired of being this radiant color show of creative intelligence, and had decided to experiment with other life forms. Melinar had been so proud of her for being brave enough to venture forth and choose the body of a female, a blue Pleiadian female to be exact.

Now he was paying her a visit. Inanna felt a sweet innocent pleasure that Melinar had thought of her. Life had been so different in that dimension, not at all like the reality of the squabbling, quarreling children of Anu or the repetitious experiences of Earth.

Inanna felt nostalgic. She merged with Melinar in remembered friendship, so glad he was there. Warm tears fell over her nose, reminding her where she was. "Oh, Melinar! I am so happy to see you again. I had forgotten all about you and the dimension of geometric forms. It is so good of you to come. I did not know how much I had missed you."

Melinar replied, albeit mind-to-mind, "Inanna, you have been busy, my dear!"

Inanna blushed. She supposed Melinar knew everything about her, now that they had merged. He must know all about her failed love life and those wars she had started down on Earth. He must also know that she was trying to help the humans by incarnating with them at various simultaneous intervals and the difficulty she was having with this task. Maybe he had come to help. But what could a geometric form know about a twentieth-century American female in New York City? Or a Celtic warrior in the second century BC who made his way in the world by chopping off heads?

Melinar answered her questions. "Inanna, my dear, I have been following your adventures with great interest and I have come to offer you my assistance. Besides, I have all the time in the world and this looks like fun to me."

"Oh, *fun!* I too thought it would be fun when I made

the commitment to help, but look at my poor selves! They are having a terrible time of it. And they never listen to me. They think they are hearing voices or that they are crazy! I am at my wits' end. I would so value any assistance you could offer me."

Melinar's brilliants accelerated into their change. "My dear, we must help Gracie to her mountain. We will create a safe place for her in the cedar forest where she will live in peace and become accustomed to hearing and seeing us. She will welcome us yet, you will see. It will work now. Between the stars and the cedars, Gracie will remember and help all the others."

For the first time in a long time, Inanna laughed softly. What if? If only one of my selves would remember, if only one would turn to me in love and trust and allow me to help. If only I could defeat Marduk.

# III

# OLNWYNN

Inanna and Melinar stepped into the transparent oval and sat quietly. Inanna observed Melinar's geometric shapes which moved so quickly that, try as she might, she could not make them slow down sufficiently to make one shape distinct from the others. She could discern, however, that many of the shapes were odd. The group was made up of more than cubes, pyramids or even rhomboids. Most of the shapes were completely unknown to her, forms her memory had no name for.

Melinar reminded her that his geometry of brilliants represented a coded language. As his thoughts formed, corresponding shapes would appear full of the intricate nuances of his thought patterns. The faster his thoughts formed, the faster the geometric display shifted its patterns and a rainbow of colors responded, becoming more intense when his thoughts were more passionate or his curiosity was satisfied. He could make sounds of a spoken language, but Melinar found pure thought far more interesting, as it conveyed more than words ever could. These thoughts automatically formed themselves in Inanna's mind as *knowing*.

Inanna was very pleased to have her old friend back in her reality. For awhile the two of them simply sat and exchanged information, renewing old ties and memories. Inanna remembered how delightful it was to be a form such as Melinar. It was difficult now to think why she had wanted to leave such a pure state of beauty.

A strange raw energy intruded on their nostalgic reveries. A very tall warrior with an axe in hand stood before them. His throat was slit from ear to ear—not at all attractive. The man was obviously in shock and terribly confused.

"Who the hell are you?" he demanded.

Inanna recognized him. It was Olnwynn, one of her multidimensional selves. She had projected Olnwynn into Northern Ireland in the second century. His DNA had looked promising, but it had all gone wrong. He would never listen to her, no matter what form she took when she appeared to him. It was obvious that the form she was in now would be of no use either. Olnwynn was finding her voluptuous but firm body very appealing.

"Hey, what do we have here? You're as fine a lass as I ever laid eyes on. By the gods! Your skin is blue!"

Inanna quickly changed her hologram in Olnwynn's mind. She left Melinar in his geometric form, thinking Olnwynn might identify him as a fairy light. For herself, she assumed the guise of a Druid priest, tall and awe-inspiring, but not too rigid or judgmental.

Olnwynn gazed at the priest, confused. "Where did she go? Who the devil are you?" He was having a very bad day. He had passed out from his usual excess of mead, when a strange thing had occurred. First there had been a quick, sharp pain, and then he was floating above his strong, handsome body, looking down on a gruesome scene.

His own son was standing over Olnwynn's body holding a long, bloody, sharp-edged dagger. The bewildered son was trembling and crying in agony! Olnwynn gazed down to see his own blood gush like a river from his throat, which was open all the way across. Olnwynn was accustomed to such sights, but this was different. This was *his* throat and *his* blood.

The door flew open as Olnwynn's wife and brother rushed into the room. The wife embraced their son, thanking him for avenging her honor. Olnwynn's brother slapped the young man on his back, promising him that some day he would be King. Olnwynn's son became hysterical and he fell over the body, sobbing. "Father, I have murdered thee! Father!"

Olnwynn hovered around the body as long as his concentration would allow him to. He could see the truth of the drama: his pretty wife had been sleeping with his brother and the two of them had conspired to murder Olnwynn, take his castle and his kingdom, and put his brother on the throne. The only person who could get close enough to Olnwynn to murder him was his very own son. It had taken his wife long hours of theatrics and horrid stories of cruelty to convince her son that Olnwynn must be done away with, but finally she had succeeded. Even Olnwynn knew it had been wrong to beat her, but now he was dead and floating above what used to be his castle.

He was disgusted by the sight of the celebrations around the castle, and his son was not recovering. After a time, he felt a strange force pulling on him, and Olnwynn felt very confused. He decided to follow the pull wherever it might lead. He had never let fear get in his way. So, here he stood facing a Druid priest surrounded by what looked like fairy lights.

The Druid priest spoke: "Olnwynn, we have been expecting you. You must soothe yourself and try to be calm. You will be taken care of here. No one will judge you; you are among friends."

Inanna looked at the slit throat and decided to repair it at once, mainly because it was so hard to look at, grotesque really. Anyway, Olnwynn had suffered enough. He didn't need to walk around with his gullet hanging out to remind him things hadn't gone so well.

Olnwynn felt his restored throat. "Say, how did you do that?" Sighing, he dropped his axe and collapsed in front of the Druid, exhausted and very thirsty. By the gods, he hadn't had anything to drink in three days. Or was it three years?

The priest spoke again: "Now, Olnwynn, perhaps we should review your memory data. Are you feeling strong enough for such an experience?"

"Am I dead?" Olnwynn asked.

*It's always the same,* Inanna explained to Melinar. *They don't even know that they are dead, and I have to gradually get them comfortable in their new state. It's a lot more work than I thought it would be.*

"Yes, Olnwynn, you are dead. But as you can see, it is only your body that is dead. You—that is to say, your conscious being and your total life experience—are here with us in another dimension. It is not so bad."

"Can you get me a drink? Wine, mead? Anything will suffice." Olnwynn's fondness for drink had been the source of many of his troubles, but Inanna produced a horn of mead for the shaken warrior. He quaffed it down like there was no tomorrow, which for him there wasn't. He noticed that it didn't taste right, and it didn't make him feel pleasantly numb the way it usually did, but he was glad to have had it anyway and asked for another.

The Druid priest spoke: "There will be plenty of time for that. Let us now get to your story, your adventure in the time/space continuum. We have a job to do, you know."

"A job. What job? No one told me anything about a job. I was just living my life when my own son murdered me! I've lost my kingdom and my life. What do you mean about a bloody job?"

"Calm yourself. Let us look at your life, Olnwynn." A hologram surrounded them, big as life, and the priest and Olnwynn watched as time unfolded before them.

Inanna had been following the amorous adventures of a Druid priestess in second century BC Ireland. In the north-western section of the island, a race of beings lived in a wild, remote landscape, and there they worshipped Nature. High sea cliffs, strong winds, and green forests gave a poetic, mystical flavor to this wild and beautiful land. Its people loved the untamed beauty of their land; they were passion-ate and warlike.

Inanna had determined to be born as a man through a Druid priestess who was of her ancient lineage. Centuries ago, the girl's ancestors had come from one of the many children Inanna had produced through her Sacred Marriage Ceremonies. This priestess was in love with a great and noble warrior, but he was married. Their passion soon pro-duced a male child, but the small priestess died in birthing him. The father never claimed him as his own, and so Olnwynn, one of Inanna's multidimensional selves, was born an orphan with no one to care for him. The Druids had taken him and made him a serving boy.

Even as a child, Olnwynn was very handsome, and from the time he could walk he charmed everyone around him. He teased the women with his smile and made them laugh. It seemed no one could resist him, and the entire village adopted him. Olnwynn had been born with the gift of being able to spontaneously speak in rhyme. This talent was honored as a sign that Olnwynn was loved by the gods, as indeed he was, especially by Inanna.

Olnwynn grew strong and tall, a beautiful man with outrageous blond curls who was seducing the ladies as soon as he could. But it was his expertise with the axe that won him his fame and fortune. In battle, Olnwynn would go into a sort of trance, becoming a force, and in a frenzy of fearlessness, he cut down foe after foe, chopping their heads off with one clean cut from his axe. As his reputation grew, people came to think of him as a god. It was whispered that the gods had fathered this orphan, and that he was immortal.

Anyone who knew Olnwynn's reputation feared to approach him in battle. He also challenged any who spoke in rhyme to a competition, and he always won. As he continued to defeat everyone in rhyme and in battle, it was only natural that the local people soon declared him their King. He moved into the big castle, adding his collection of severed heads to the surrounding castle wall, a quaint custom. You might imagine the ghastly specter of such a wall would encourage a passing warlord to stop and think before attacking.

Olnwynn had always loved to drink anything. Now that he was King, there was no one to stop him from his drinking, or from doing anything else he wanted to do. He answered to no one. Without much effort, he had all the women he wanted; they practically threw themselves at him. No one could believe it when he finally married. They all said his wife must have bewitched him or put herbs in his mead. It was true that this pretty young girl came from a long line of witches; some dared to whisper that the power of her sexual allure came from magic. She wanted Olnwynn, but she also wanted wealth and position, and she gave Olnwynn the son he had demanded.

One day, a man who resembled Olnwynn showed up at the castle gate claiming to be the son of the great warrior who was rumored to have fathered Olnwynn. They did look a great deal alike, although Olnwynn was far more handsome and much taller than this mysterious new brother.

Olnwynn was basically trusting, and he took the brother in, glad to have someone to drink and carouse with. It would be good for his son to have an uncle, and this brother was rich, an asset to his court. Olnwynn barely noticed the electricity between his pretty little wife and his new brother, but everyone else did. The brother also spent many hours with Olnwynn's son, teaching him swordsmanship and history. It was quite a family, for awhile.

Inanna, who had incarnated into Olnwynn and was simultaneously watching him as her total self, began to see that she was losing the battle with his lower nature. The powerful programming contained in his flesh and blood came to rule him. Spirit was being swamped by matter and the five senses. During this period, Inanna made special attempts to distract and inspire Olnwynn. She appeared to him as a dragon, a god, a goddess (big mistake!), and finally an ancient warrior. She encouraged him to go off by himself, to contemplate the source of his poetry and his greatness. But even when she could get him to listen, which wasn't very often, even when he would make her promises and agree to do thus and so, he would just immediately go off and get drunk, forgetting everything they had discussed. It was enormously frustrating for her.

Olnwynn had the perfect set of recessive genes. He was gifted, he could have accessed all the dimensions even while living in his human body, and he could have brought enlightening frequencies onto the planet Earth. But, no! He preferred to get drunk and seduce women!

What a colossal waste! Inanna almost stopped following his life. It was so boring and repetitive, and eventually even his poetry became dull.

Marriage didn't keep Olnwynn from his ladies. He was inclined to think anyone in skirts belonged to him, if only for a night. You can imagine the scenes in the castle with his wife. She was possessed of a fiery temper, and she unleashed it upon Olnwynn whenever it suited her. As the years passed, she became more and more of a whining shrew; she even began to get on Inanna's nerves. You couldn't blame the woman, but, by the gods, her jealous tirades and wild tantrums were more than anyone in the castle could bear. Everyone knew that Olnwynn was naughty, but he had always been that way, and he was so charming and handsome. They saw his wife as a witch, and thought it was no wonder he fooled around.

Then the drink started to have its inevitable ugly

effects on Olnwynn's mind. He began to deteriorate. He took to beating his wife when she railed at him. He was big, she was little, and the scenes got ugly. She would run to Olnwynn's brother, crying and showing the blood and her bruises. In time, she succeeded in turning her son, Olnwynn's brother, and most of the court against their King.

Olnwynn became more and more violent. Each night he drank himself into a stupor, passing into oblivion. He was carried nightly into his bedroom by his faithful servant, who would have killed anyone who tried to touch his King. Olnwynn had saved this man's life in battle many times. No one would have dared to attack Olnwynn face to face; even drunk, he was still formidable. There was only one who would be allowed to enter the King's bedroom, and that was his son. Olnwynn's wife knew that her only chance to kill her husband was to convince their son to slit his throat while he lay helpless.

Olnwynn stared vacantly at the hologram of his life. Inanna almost became herself again, but quickly shifted back into the form of the familiar Druid priest. "And so, my son, you see how things have gone for you."

Unable to get his bearings at first, Olnwynn felt dizzied by the transparent movie playing out before him. He didn't want to see again the part where his blood gushed out of his throat. The priest shut off the replay, and all was quiet for a few endless moments.

Regaining some composure, Olnwynn spoke. "So what was all this about a job to do?"

At least his curiosity wasn't dead.

# IV

# LOST MOUNTAIN

Gracie wanted a drink. She preferred a French red, but tonight anything would do. Lost Mountain was a long way from New York City. She was beginning to get used to the silence, but she felt a little vulnerable without the layers of noise and activity that had given her a false sense of security in the city. Snuggled into her log cabin with her two dogs, Gracie told herself that being alone on this mountain was much safer than being anywhere in that city.

A person can be as alone in New York City as they can on Lost Mountain, she told herself. There had been days in the city when she had spoken to no one. Gracie had always been a loner. Born into a wealthy family in the Old South, she had always felt as if she had somehow been mistakenly delivered to the wrong family! It had been easy for her to believe that she might indeed be an alien from space, because she had never felt comfortable on Earth; there was an empty feeling inside her that never left her. It was as if she knew she didn't belong here and she longed to go home, *whatever* that was.

Gracie had traveled a lot, moved around, married, divorced, joined groups, left them, and read too many books. No one had the answers she was looking for. She had read that the monks in Tibet sealed themselves up in dark cells for a year at a time, talking to no one. She was ready to do the same, in her own way.

Pouring herself a glass of California merlot, Gracie contemplated her childhood. Her father owned and developed shopping malls, not the enormous ones that take over everything, but those little ones that pop up everywhere to contribute their aesthetic to the suburban blight. He was very rich and busy, too busy for his daughter. Everyone told her she should be happy and grateful; she had all the money in the world, she went to the finest private school for young ladies, and could charge her clothes whenever she liked in the best stores.

Her brother was perfectly happy, confident he would take over his father's business when he grew up and take his place in the world as a shining example of the American Dream. But, Gracie wondered, if everything was so wonderful, then why did her mother take so many pills?

Gracie's mother, Diana, was a southern belle from the old school. Her own mother had died when she was only four years old, and little Diana had blamed herself. As a young woman Diana had tried to be independent, but in her late thirties she married Gracie's father, Brent, both for love and to escape from the vagaries of being a woman alone. In his way, Brent adored Diana, but he was a natural tyrant. If Diana got out of line, Brent's considerable temper would unleash itself. The medicine cabinet in Diana's bathroom was loaded with tranquilizers and sleeping pills, what came to be known as "mother's little helpers."

Gracie was not immune to her father's temper either. If she got in his way or dared to disagree with his plans for her life, he would fly into a rage, endlessly degrading her with verbal abuse. Silently, her mother would head for the medicine cabinet as Gracie was reduced to a sobbing heap. No one ever defended Gracie or stood up for her. Like clockwork, to smooth things over, her father would buy her things after such an episode; a doll, a dress, and later, stocks. But Gracie never learned to see life the way her family did. She was afraid she would become a trophy for some rich tyrant if she married, and she didn't want to end up like her mother, no matter how good the pay was.

Gracie's life in high school was equally unhappy. Even though she was pretty and had boyfriends, there was a part of her that no one knew or, it seemed, even wanted to know. Rebelling, she began to seek out people who were unacceptable to her family and formed friendships with artists and musicians. It was the sixties, and Gracie ran away to New York City, a breath of fresh air for her!

It was really quiet in that lonely mountain cabin. Even the coyotes had finally stopped their crazy howling. There was no moon at all, only the stars. Gracie decided to sleep out on the deck under the sky. In her bluejeans and sweater, she crawled into her warm sleeping bag and looked up. God! You could see every star in the sky, and there were millions of them! This was definitely not like the city! It was so pristine and beautiful. Gracie forgot about her past, her loneliness, her fear, and lost herself in the beauty of the night sky.

Inanna, still in the guise of a Druid priest, spoke to Olnwynn. "My son, you may rest for awhile now. We can talk later."

The peace and calm that was coming from Gracie floated into Inanna's reality. "Melinar, now is our chance. What can we say? What shall we do? We don't want to frighten her."

Melinar's brilliants began to accelerate.

Tears formed in Gracie's big brown eyes. The beauty of the night sky was too much for her. She had not seen such a sky for many years, and as a shooting star passed before her, Gracie smiled. A good omen, she thought. This is my place, this is where I belong, and I will find what I am looking for here.

The starry sky was so bright that Gracie closed her eyes. Behind her lids, she saw the total blackness of the Eye of her Mind. She wondered at the contrast, until a colorful object formed in that blackness and began to gyrate. Many exquisitely beautiful geometric forms, like precious gems, were moving and mutating in front of her. It was fun to watch such a thing, and Gracie hoped it wouldn't go away. She didn't know what this light show could mean, but instinctively she loved it.

Gracie had always had visions. Even as a child she had imaginary friends. One was a tiny alien from outer space. Her friendly alien would fly around in the most amazing vehicle and follow beside her father's car when the family traveled. The alien would tell Gracie all kinds of interesting stories, explaining things to her, keeping her occupied for hours. Later, Gracie wished she could recall anything he had said to her. Why did she forget? She had felt so close to him, felt he was teaching her so many things she really needed to know. Why could she not remember them now?

The mutating jewels continued to dance before her as long as Gracie could remain awake. She felt safe. At last the wine and the night sky ushered her into sleep, thinking that tomorrow she would go for a long walk in the cedar forest. The rich scent of the cedars drifted into her awareness as she fell fast asleep.

Melinar smiled. "You see, my Inanna, we will help her to feel safe and at one with the sky and the forest. Her fears will melt into the Earth and she will open herself to us. We will teach her to love herself, and that love will give her the courage to *know*."

Inanna gazed over at Olnwynn, who was snoring rather loudly. She was constantly amazed at the antics of her multidimensional selves. These beings were of her DNA, and she had somewhere in time been half of the origin of all of them. But finding herself among all the ensuing clutter these selves managed to create proved to be an ongoing challenge. Yet, somewhere in all of the selves lay the dormant ability to be whatever they wanted to be. Each one possessed the power to think for himself or herself; each was an information gatherer for Prime Creator.

With their DNA only partially activated, her multidimensional selves were trapped in a sort of electronic prison of experiences that repeated over and over, as though the entire planet were doomed to an eternal rewind. The human species was famous all over the galaxy for its inability to learn from its adventures. Tyrants and wars came and went, yet no one seemed the wiser for it. Inanna knew the keeper of this prison all too well. For most of her Pleiadian life she had been at odds with her cousin Marduk.

Marduk had successfully defeated all the other members of the family of Anu, and now controlled not only Earth, but also their home planet, Nibiru, and the entire Pleiadian star system. His tyranny was supreme and his methods ingenious. Marduk was quite the egotist as well as being completely heartless, and he had cloned a vast army of soldiers who all resembled him. He thrived on the pain and frustration of those he conquered and ruled. Worst of all, the inhabitants of Earth did not even know who their jailer was. Believing they had committed some unforgivable sin, humans blamed themselves for their sad state, which means they blamed each other.

Using the subtle means of brainwashing propaganda, Marduk fomented antagonism among groups of people. Families, tribes, nations—no group was too large or too small to be manipulated. Whenever a good new idea was brought forth, some were encouraged to follow and support it while an equal number would be whipped up against it. The idea might be religious or political, or even just the idea of crossing an ocean. With an unplugged brain which functioned at one-tenth of its capacity, the humans, instead of reasoning for themselves, would only react, often violently, to Marduk's subtle manipulations. War was easily started in such fertile conditions.

Religious wars were Marduk's favorite, but he wasn't above *any* potential hostility. A type of mind which did not readily produce original thoughts, but only reacted to others, came to dominate, and repetitive behavior engraved itself into the genetic codes of the human race through the emotion of fear. No one was allowed to remember for very long that all humans had originally come from the same source, and those who suggested such ideas were laughed at or brutally destroyed in short order. No one remembered that the source of all life was the Love of Prime Creator.

Inanna thought about her own part in this ongoing deception. She and the family of Anu had behaved badly; like spoiled children they had all followed their own selfish whims, never considering the consequences. Without knowing it, the family had created Marduk, the perfect result of their self-centered bickering and aggression. It was not much of a legacy.

If the entire family of Anu had not found itself surrounded by the invisible *Wall*, they probably would have just continued in their own selfish, controlling ways. But *The Wall* had the effect of stopping the ongoing evolution of each and every member of the family, Inanna included. She had never been so bored. It was as if all the excitement and spontaneity had been erased from their lives. Having no other choice, all that was left for the family of Anu was to repair the damage they had done on Earth. For *The Wall* to disappear, the human species had to be freed from its wheel of repetition so that they could once again begin to evolve, and cease to worship the god whose name they didn't even know, Marduk.

So Inanna and many other family members had chosen to project varying portions of themselves into bodies in multiple time frames. They were hoping that any one of these multidimensional selves might activate the missing genes of the species and create a potential for total change on Earth. Alas, their hopes were beginning to fade, as this task was proving arduous at best.

It did no good to tell the humans they had been taken over by an alien race almost 500,000 years ago, and it was equally useless to tell them their DNA had been partially unplugged. Marduk had been very successful in debunking all such ideas from the beginning, and anyone who expressed them was totally ridiculed. The humans were so naturally insecure that they easily gave up trying to tell anyone anything that didn't conform to the general consensus. Anyone who saw or heard anything that everyone else did not also see or hear was met with derision, often institutionalized, and in some periods, burned at the stake.

Television and, later, computers, became the prime tools in conditioning and focusing the thoughts of the masses. The "information highway" made it easy for Marduk to control the group mind of the entire planet. Indeed televisions and computer monitors had become like altars in each home as people sat before them for hours, filling their minds with Marduk's propaganda. Possessions increased and engulfed people as they got deeper in debt, struggling to be like the beautiful and wealthy on TV. Most homes had at least three such altars. All of the human race wanted to be rich, and the rich and powerful were revered regardless of their character or behavior.

The electronic frequencies that enveloped Terra made it almost impossible for Inanna and her family to communicate with their multidimensional selves, because no one was listening.

Inanna watched little Gracie sleep. Gracie's dogs reminded her of the pet lions she had loved so devotedly on Terra. The dogs became alert as Inanna's consciousness focused on them. Perhaps, she thought, I will be able to get through to Gracie. Inanna allowed herself to feel hopeful as she scanned the life data of her other selves.

# V

# THE KEEPER OF
# THE CRYSTALS

Into the time of Atlantis, Inanna had projected a part of herself as the incarnation of a priest named Atilar. This multidimensional self would provide her with a life experience of knowledge that could only come from self-mastery. She reasoned that Atilar's life would by osmosis affect her other multidimensional selves, as all of her selves affected one another. One highly developed psyche would do the others a world of good.

Atilar's genes had been carefully cultivated for many generations. He contained the DNA of Inanna's father, thus giving her entry access. He was born in the power centers of Atlantis and had been given at birth to the priests of the Order of the Blue Robes. His entire early life was spent in rigorous training to carry out the sole task of maintaining the frequencies of Atlantis' great crystal center by the use of thought.

All of Atlantis was powered by the spirals of crystal which were guarded and maintained by the Order of the Blue Robes. As a child, Atilar was told he had been bred for this single purpose. He would never know a woman, he would never marry, and he would never experience life as an ordinary human. His life had been decided and dedicated to this sacred task eons ago.

When other children were playing ball, Atilar was seated in a full lotus position, not moving an eyelid for hours. He was trained to ignore his body and any pain or distraction he might experience. He was taught the martial arts, but only for the purpose of protecting the crystals and activating the force that in your time is called the *chi*. In Atlantis no one ever named this force. As the great minds of Atlantis knew that many forces exist which cannot be named, this force was referred to with a sound. Atilar was trained to access this powerful force from his loins and to bring this energy up through the seven invisible centers of his body to empower his mind and his will.

Atilar never regretted his fate. From childhood he had been told how special and privileged he was, and he reveled in the ecstatic feeling he was able to generate in his being by harnessing the subtle forces of his body and connecting them to the cosmos through the crystals. For Atilar and the priests of the Order of the Blue Robes, there was only one missing piece; they did not know Love. Their focus was on the mind and its power, but none of them had ever experienced Love. Foolishly, they regarded it as unimportant. Never accessing its power, Love remained beyond them, and for this reason, they were limited.

Atilar sat before the crystals and gazed deeply at their beauty, uniting his consciousness with each exquisite shard in order to modulate its resonance. The crystals were transducers of energy and Atilar was their tuner. He had not allowed himself to move for seven days. He had slowed his heart down to the required cycles and had blocked any awareness of pain from the receptors in his brain. Pain as information would not be registered.

For a moment, Atilar allowed himself to journey completely out of his body. He was now past fifty, but his body did not show it. He was lean and hard, with long graying hair and almond-shaped eyes so light in color they were almost gold. Atilar was an accomplished traveler and enjoyed his occasional adventures. In his consciousness, he spun the *Merkaba* which surrounded his body and began to move through space. Flying past galactic nebulae, he thrilled to the beauty and sensation of being absolutely free. He moved toward a planet that at first appeared to be empty, but on closer examination showed pools of metallic liquid forming into beings who smiled a greeting to him. The universe was truly filled with wonders!

Silently, Qi, the Master of the Order of the Blue Robes, entered the chamber. "Atilar, it is time for you to rest. You have completed this frequency modulation to perfection, and now you must recharge yourself."

Reluctantly, Atilar relaxed into his body. "As you wish, Master Qi."

Atilar had served Qi from his early childhood and was Master Qi's favorite pupil. Master Qi had been very hard on him, because he knew of Atilar's genetic potential and because he hoped Atilar would one day take his place as the Master of the Order of the Blue Robes.

Master Qi spoke: "When you have rested, my son, I want you to come to the gateway area to meet a newcomer. A girl child has been brought to us from the Priestesses of the Moon. This child is a rare genetic hybrid, and her potential to empower the crystals will be interesting to observe."

Atilar nodded. These females were necessary to create a balance in the predominantly male energies in the power center, but they were almost always the same. They had been bred to generate the invisible forces, but were not allowed to think for themselves. Because their education was limited, they were never of much interest to Atilar; he saw them much as one might see a transistor or a car battery.

Atilar retired to his pristine cell and fell into a deep sleep, hoping to return to his metallic liquid planet and continue his visit with the beings there.

Inanna and Melinar focused their awareness back to Gracie. Already knowing Atilar's future, they desired only to bring his abilities to the other multidimensional selves. As Gracie woke up, Melinar projected an image into her waking consciousness.

Still half asleep, Gracie struggled with her sleeping bag. The morning dew and the morning light were starting to make her uncomfortable. In her netherworld state, she had glimpsed a room filled with spiraling crystals, and a man with long gray hair, a white shirt and black trousers, who was rising to leave the room. He was oddly familiar to Gracie, but she could not place where or when she might have known him. Certainly, he possessed more dignity than the men of her own times.

The cold gray light of morning forced her to open

her eyes. Gracie had never slept outside in the Pacific Northwest before. Her sleeping bag was drenched with dew and her feet were freezing. Gracie's beloved dogs trotted over to kiss her face in their usual morning greeting. In the city, an elevator ride separated the pups from their early-morning walk. Gracie laughed, thinking that if she always slept outside, she would never have to let the dogs out!

She retreated to the kitchen to fire up the woodstove. Reaching for the familiar red and yellow can of coffee, Gracie saw it was nearly empty. In New York City, she had grown fond of this Puerto Rican roast, but now she would have to find a new coffee. She poured herself a cup of espresso with lots of hot milk and some honey.

Gracie's cabin was located in a little valley on Lost Mountain, and from her window she could see the Olympic Mountains. Near the cabin was a thick cedar forest; the mountains stretched behind her, and the Strait of Juan de Fuca lay far below. Being so isolated in Nature was intoxicating.

Gracie grabbed a warm jacket and headed for the forest with her pups. As she walked along the trail, she remembered another time.

As a child, Gracie had loved summer camp, and for five years she had escaped the confinement of her family's life at a girls' summer camp in the southern hills of her state. There she had taken to walking by herself, using the excuse that she loved to draw trees. In truth, she loved being alone in Nature.

Gracie remembered walking down a similar trail at her camp when she was only seven years old. Suddenly, for no reason, she had stopped and looked up at the sky. There had been a few puffy white clouds against the pure blue. "Can I come home now?" Gracie had asked. A voice had answered her, "No, not yet."

Gracie had never really known whom she was talking to, or what *home* she wanted to return to. It was only one of the many unsolved mysteries of her life. Surely she had never felt at home anywhere on Earth. Her parents' home had been suffocating to her, and she had been a virtual gypsy since leaving there. Restlessly, Gracie moved every two years, never feeling at home anywhere or with anyone.

Deep in the woods now, Gracie stood beside an enormous old cedar and wrapped her arms around it. She put her face close to the bark and inhaled deeply. The smells were indescribably pure and refreshing; she wished she could drink the tree. A gentle breeze caressed her face, and she felt so calm and happy.

Gracie sat down. She knew she didn't need to sit in the lotus position, but she had done so for many years and it was the most natural choice for her. She leaned her back against the tree and dug her hands down into the forest floor. There was nothing as sweet as this in any city, she mused. Moving her consciousness into a meditative state, Gracie let her eyes unfocus. Ever since she had been a small child in church, she had been able to turn everything in her field of vision into subtle, vibrating gold light. It was fun, beautiful, and it always made her feel good.

Today there was more than light. Between two tall cedars stood three beings. They were not solid as you would see a person; rather, they were energy that could be made out as form, and a glow of light surrounded that form. Gracie was a little frightened, but immensely curious.

Inanna noticed that Olnwynn had followed her and Melinar into the forest to meet with Gracie. Oh, no! What might he do? Inanna was glad she had tidied up that slit throat, the sight of which certainly would have frightened little Gracie. Inanna gave Olnwynn a threatening glance to keep him quiet, but she had forgotten to assume the form of the Druid for Olnwynn, and he wasn't paying much attention to her.

"What do we have here? A little lassie all alone in the forest with two fine wolves and no axe!" Olnwynn exclaimed.

"Who are you?" Gracie asked.

"Don't pay any mind to him, he is just getting used to being in a new world," Inanna interjected. "We have come to this ancient forest to be with you. We have come to be your friends, your companions. You will not be lonely anymore, and we will help you to know that which you seek."

Melinar assumed the form of a gentle older man with very kind eyes, while retaining some effects of the mutating brilliants. He spoke to Gracie. "My child, you have come to Earth for a reason. It is not your true home, and you are more than you believe yourself to be. You have been many other expressions in many other worlds, and you have come here by choice to assist. There is a great change coming to this planet. The more humans who can prepare for this shift, the easier it will be for all. You have chosen to help in this moment."

It was as if something Gracie had held inside her started to break free, and her little body began to shake with held emotions. Soon she was sobbing and crying as the release of old feelings passed through her physical body and left her somehow lighter. Unable to sit up any longer, she lay down on the forest floor. She felt all her emotional pain from this lifetime, and perhaps others, sink deep into the soil beneath her, as the Earth and the forest healed her.

Inanna spoke tenderly. "Gracie, whenever you want us

to talk to you, come to this place. We will be here. You will become accustomed to our friendship, and soon you will find us wherever you are. But you must invite us in; you must want us. We will be waiting, as we have waited all of your life for you to ask us for assistance. You must open the doors to us. We love you."

Gracie shivered and looked around. The dogs had been perfectly still, not minding the visitors in the least. Whoever had been there was gone now, and Gracie was getting very hungry. Walking back to the cabin, she wondered if her new friends were one and the same with the voice in the clouds she had heard as a child. She sighed. A steaming bowl of chicken noodle soup would taste so good right now. The dogs hurried their steps.

Inanna glanced at Melinar. "Do you think we frightened her?"

Melinar answered, "No, but it was enough for one day and we must go slowly. You know how the humans can react to too much energy and knowledge. It can retard them in fear for lifetimes."

Yes, Inanna had seen that happen too often. It seemed the humans could only withstand small doses, but time was running out; the year 2011 wasn't very far off. Inanna knew she must speak to Olnwynn. If he insisted on accompanying them, he must be taught what was going on. Perhaps he might prove useful; he was after all, fearless and clever.

# VI

# THE NON-EXISTENT PAST

Inanna and Melinar returned to the oval. A central point of focus for them, it helped to maintain some order in the juggling of all the dimensional time shifts. Going back and forth in time can be confusing for even the most skilled practitioner. Now and then Inanna was tempted to imagine that the past was the past, or that her multidimensional selves were sequential. At such moments, Melinar would remind Inanna to get a grip on herself and to remember that in the mind of Prime Creator, time does not exist, and that all her incarnations were simultaneous.

It was Melinar who noticed the missing Olnwynn. Inanna gazed around her realities and found the tall warrior still standing in the ancient cedar forest. The place reminded him of his homeland in old northern Ireland. Olnwynn was heartbroken and homesick. He thought of his son. There were so many things he missed, so many things left undone. Why had he become so violent, so cruel to those he loved?

Inanna emitted a sort of magnetic rubber band in her consciousness and gently pulled Olnwynn back into the oval. Olnwynn reacted to his new surroundings with an angry outburst. In truth, he had known fear, but he had always expressed it as anger. He demanded to know where he was, and who they were.

Inanna turned to Melinar. They both agreed to show themselves to Olnwynn as radiant photon beings, a form which seemed to please all humans. Keeping the shape of humans, their bodies were made up of cascading shooting photons displaying a vast array of golden colors of changing lights. It was quite beautiful to witness.

Olnwynn gazed at the forms and felt comforted. He calmed down a bit. Inanna was a little tired, however, and kept losing it. She *shape-shifted* from the photon being to the Druid priest and back to her voluptuous blue female Pleiadian self. This naturally agitated Olnwynn, who was having enough trouble adjusting to his new reality.

"That does it!" Olnwynn raged. "I insist on being told the truth. Who are you and what am I doing here?"

Melinar volunteered an answer. "You are that which we are. Specifically, you are her." Melinar pointed to Inanna, who had given up on shape-shifting for the moment and had settled down into her favorite blue body.

Olnwynn remained incredulous. The idea of being a blue female was totally foreign to him, although she was rather lovely in an alien sort of way, and she did seem oddly familiar. He had seen many visions in his time, but lately it had been difficult to sort them out from his permanent state of inebriation. He was so fond of drink.

Melinar continued in a hopeful manner. "We are that which you are. This is the Lady Inanna who has created you, so to speak. A part of herself has gone forth into the time/space continuum to form you, Olnwynn. You have perceived yourself as a separate entity because you were so designed, but that separation is an illusion. Your consciousness and life data will be reabsorbed back into the whole, as all data is eventually absorbed into the mind of Prime Creator. In reality, none of us has ever left the mind of Prime Creator."

Olnwynn didn't like that "reabsorbed" nonsense one little bit. It made him think of things like annihilation or oblivion.

Reading Olnwynn's thoughts, Melinar continued, "No, my son, you will not be annihilated. You and your consciousness will remain intact. You will simply become part of a greater body of data, while still *being* the Olnwynn self which is familiar to you. The Lady Inanna has created you for a purpose, and that purpose is to serve in the liberation of the human species."

The only way Olnwynn could recall liberating anybody was by chopping off their heads! Plus, he didn't like the concept of having been created by a woman for some purpose he knew nothing about. On Earth he had been a king, and he wasn't used to being controlled. He began to complain. Was he merely the pawn in someone's game? Had he been the plaything of someone he didn't even know existed, no matter how appealing she was just now?

Melinar suggested that Olnwynn take a seat while he explained. "Almost 500,000 years past, a group of space travelers from a star system called the Pleiades established a mining colony on planet Earth. They were a family grouping from an overlord named Anu. They lived on an artificial planet which orbits though this solar system every 3,600 years. The family of Anu came to Earth to extract gold for their own atmosphere, which was becoming depleted from their frequent radiation wars. The family was a disagreeable lot, prone to go to war at the slightest provocation.

"Once the mining colony was established, it became apparent more workers would be required for the mining operations. So the scientists in the family of Anu, a sister and a brother named Ninhursag and Enki, took a humanoid species which lived on Earth at that time and manipulated its genetic material. They produced a race of workers who have been the primary inhabitants of your planet ever since."

Olnwynn was astonished. He had heard of such things, as a young boy, from the secret teachings of the Druids, but had forgotten them as he matured and began to slaughter his fellows for power. There were many myths about the Druids having come from a magical kingdom called Atlantis. According to the Druids, there had been a great war, Atlantis had disappeared under the sea, and her inhabitants had migrated to the islands Olnwynn had grown up in.

"So does this mean that I have been nothing but one of a race of slaves?" The idea was particularly repulsive to Olnwynn. On the other hand, he was thinking it might be fun to conquer an entire planet—all those heads.

Melinar endeavored to steer Olnwynn's consciousness into a more uplifted state. "No, my son. You were created by the Lady Inanna to rescue the race of workers. One member of the family of Anu, a male by the name of Marduk, now controls Earth. This entity, Marduk, and his legions refuse to let the humans go. We desire to return the human race to its original abilities, to plug in its genetic codes, and to allow humans their own natural evolution as was intended

180

by Prime Creator."

Olnwynn wasn't exactly sure what genetic codes were, but he was getting the drift. Inanna was giving him access to any information he would open his consciousness to, without swamping him. Olnwynn began to get a feeling for this Marduk, having himself warred against tyrants in varying forms countless times on the battlefields of his homeland. As a young man, Olnwynn had vowed to fight tyranny wherever it might be found, until it seemed he had become a tyrant himself. Such thoughts made Olnwynn feel sad.

From out of thin air, there appeared a regal old man riding on an enormous green and golden dragon. Olnwynn had only seen paintings of such dragons and was a bit startled. But Inanna transferred the necessary information to Olnwynn's mind, and he opened himself up to the visitors.

Inanna spoke. "Olnwynn, this is my great-uncle, Enki. Enki is one of the creators of the human species, and this is his favorite dragon, Puffy."

Enki smiled. He was always pleased to see Inanna, and he knew Melinar well. Enki was also projecting portions of himself into the human species at various time points. He had committed all his energies to rescuing the species he had created—rescuing it from the clutches of his own son, Marduk. For Enki, there was a great deal at stake.

Enki spoke to Inanna's multidimensional self. "Olnwynn, I have come especially to visit you. I have admired you greatly from a distance. I, too, have been overly fond of drink and the women of Earth; the combination can be so pleasing. Why if I had been as handsome as you, boy, I would have..."

Inanna and Melinar simultaneously delivered a fierce frown to Enki.

"But I have also admired your boundless courage," Enki

181

continued. "Courage is what we require now. It will take much courage for the children of Earth to believe the truth, and they must learn these things soon. A great change is coming on their planet, and we desire to instruct them in this change so they will not be afraid. From you, Olnwynn, they could receive this courage to *know*, to know the truth."

Olnwynn thought to himself how it would be a pleasure to fight this Marduk and his legions. Olnwynn loved a good battle, and he found the longer he was separated from his land, the more he loved it and all the folk who lived there. He longed to embrace his son, and he even missed his pretty wife. He wished he hadn't treated her so badly; perhaps someday he could make it up to her. Yes, and it would be good to fight this Marduk, to set the people free from tyrants everywhere.

"I vow to assist in the defeat of this tyrant! I will give courage to any and all who ask. You can all count on Olnwynn!"

Inanna smiled at the big handsome warrior. All the energy she had put into this passionate man might not be lost after all. Melinar reminded her that nothing is ever lost.

"Well, Olnwynn, that is fine," Inanna spoke softly. "But you had better get used to time traveling!"

VII

# SOME INTERACTION

Inanna watched as Enki and his dragon faded back into their own reality. Inanna loved Enki, and she never really blamed him for what had happened, but occasionally it did cross her mind that if only Enki had been able to stand up to his son, Marduk, she might still be the reigning Queen of Sumer. However, the truth was that the entire family had contributed to the creation of Marduk, and after all was said and done, Marduk was as much a part of Prime Creator as any of them. They were all a part of the grand cosmic play, the balance between the so-called forces of light and dark. Now, it was up to her and the rest of the family of Anu to make the necessary adjustments in the balance of power.

Olnwynn was beginning to get a feel for what was going on. He realized that this woman had come to Earth from the stars and had somehow magically projected a part of herself into many different bodies in order to create him, and how many more he didn't know. He understood that her composite group was designed to help liberate the inhabitants of Earth from a tyrant whose name was Marduk. There were obviously more missing pieces.

"Are there more of us out there?" Olnwynn asked.

"Yes," Inanna replied. She quickly scanned a few of her current selves and their data banks.

"I think I am beginning to understand," Olnwynn mused. "When I was a child, you were the one who spoke to me. Later on, it was you who inspired me with poetry, and all those visions I had came from you. If only I had listened to you, I might have remembered."

Inanna was kind. "I did not do everything; you were very courageous at every turn. You came from a rich lineage with unlimited potential, and you realized much of it. It was my idea to leave you an orphan so you would turn to me. I forgot how powerfully alcohol can block off any psychic communication. And you lived in an environment of fear and endless wars perpetrated by my cousin, the tyrant Marduk. Do not blame yourself; rather, think on what you have learned."

Olnwynn, Inanna, and Melinar turned their attention to Gracie. Olnwynn had never seen a woman so brave as to go live alone in the forest, and he admired her wolves.

"Dogs, Olnwynn, they are beautiful dogs," Melinar corrected. "You can help Gracie, you can inspire her with your courage. Come, let us be near her."

Gracie had not forgotten her experience in the forest, and she vowed to meditate between three and four o'clock every morning. She made up her mind to do what she called "the desert," which to Gracie meant no telephone calls, no television, no newspapers. She would allow herself to listen to certain kinds of music and read a few inspiring books like *The Mahabharata*, the *Tao Teh Ching* of Lao-Tzu, or *The Tibetan Book of the Dead*.

Gracie had read about the float tank that was designed by John Lilly, the scientist who spoke with the dolphins. Deciding to invent her own float tank, she filled her bath almost to the top and put candles around the sides. In the candlelit darkness, she lay in the water, arching her back with only her nose above the water level. There she would remain floating for hours until the water became so cold it distracted her. Then Gracie would go into a room and meditate. She had an inexpensive electronic keyboard with a button she could push to hold one note as long as the batteries would last. Gracie would do this, and listen endlessly to the one tone while she focused her consciousness.

The first three days of the "the desert" were always the hardest. There was something in Gracie that would have done anything to make a phone call, or to watch even the stupidest television program those first three days. But if she held fast to her resolve, the rewards were great. Afterward, everything in her surroundings emanated beauty, and her spirit guides came close to her. It was wonderful; these moments of beauty were the happiest times of her life. Gracie had walked her "desert" before to find peace. It was her version of pretending to be in a monastery, high in the Himalayas in Tibet.

Once she had been with a film crew in England who were filming a documentary on Tibetan music. She had been truly thrilled to be in the presence of those monks; the sounds from their bells and great horns had lifted her into her golden light. But when it was over, she had ignorantly come too close to their sacred altar. She did not know that in their belief, if she had been menstruating, her touch would have made their altar impure. She was told it would have taken them six months to purify it. The monks had restrained her from getting any closer, and the experience had hurt and confused Gracie. That day she had lost interest in traveling to Tibet. She realized she would not find there what she sought. Gracie knew instinctively that the same blood which brought forth life, could never be impure!

Sitting in front of her meditation table, Gracie slipped into another reality. She had recalled her other lives before. It was as if suddenly she could see through the eyes of another being, and as she stared at the hard, cold stones of what seemed to be a prison cell, a blue robe was thrown over "her" body. But it wasn't her body at all; it was a man with long gray hair, a soiled white shirt and black trousers. The man seemed to be in a state of shock.

Atilar lay motionless on the cold stone floor. Why had he done it? He, who had mastered all his impulses all of his life, found himself totally bewildered by his utter helplessness. Now everything was gone, lost, and he had no chance of recourse. He would be glad to die.

He thought of the first moment he had seen her. Master Qi had summoned him to the gateway area to meet the new girl who had been brought by the Priestesses of the Moon. It was routine, an everyday occurrence. That is, until he saw her. What was it about her? It was as if Atilar had known this girl throughout eternity, and her presence touched a sleeping part of his being, bringing him to feel as he never had before. It wasn't just that she was beautiful, which of course she was. All the girls chosen by the Order of the Moon were exquisitely lovely. But this girl was somehow different. Her skin was the color of fresh cream, and her eyes were dark blue like the sea. Her copper hair flowed down her body and touched the ground around her. However, it was her purity that sent an arrow through his soul. Being near her caused him the sweetest pain.

The tragedy began as Master Qi routinely placed the girl in Atilar's care. Why hadn't Master Qi noticed the change in his favorite student? Or had he?

The girl naturally looked up to Atilar. He was renowned all over Atlantis as the heir to Master Qi and as the most advanced in the discipline of modulating the crystals through thought. All the young novices worshipped Atilar at a distance. He thought nothing of it; such matters ordinarily did not interest him, until now.

Alone in his room, Atilar began to entertain thoughts he had never before considered. He knew that if he applied the magic he had learned over the years, he could easily seduce the girl. He also knew that magic would make the encounter one of cosmic proportions—it would be as if he and the girl were all the raw energies in the universe becoming as one. Only a man of Atilar's talents and experience could generate this kind of lovemaking. And love her he did, desperately and totally, with all his being. He had only been half alive before he met her, he knew that now; and even his torment was as ecstasy to him.

Time passed. Each day Atilar found more excuses to be with the girl. She was in his every thought. It was quite normal for a Priestess from the Order of the Moon to accompany someone like Atilar into the great hall of the spiraling crystals. Ordinarily, the girl would merely sit quietly and generate the required polarity of female energy, but one day Atilar made a suggestion.

He told the girl to sit in front of him and gaze deeply into his eyes, explaining that he was experimenting with new methods to modulate the crystals' frequencies. Obediently, the young girl placed her lovely white body in front of Atilar. She adored him, and would have done anything he asked her.

Atilar fell into the deep blue eyes of his beloved. Locked in union for hours, the two virgins exchanged their energy. As the frequencies of their bodies accelerated, they were transported into a new reality. Atilar and the girl became as *one*. The floor, the room, even Atlantis itself disappeared. All that existed was their oneness emanating power into pure light. Time and space had vanished.

If only Atilar had been content to remain in this way. But the man in him, the human, desired completion. Focusing on her copper hair and her creamy elegant throat, Atilar pushed her white robes from her shoulders. Her breasts were small and perfect, and he caressed them. Gently laying her down, Atilar allowed himself to lovingly enter her sacred sweetness. His heart was throbbing as blood rushed through his body and his passion spilled itself within her. Never had he known such happiness, such bliss. Resonating with their love, the spiraling crystals in the room began to sing, emitting tender harmonies in response to this powerful force.

The doors flew open as Master Qi and the guardians abruptly entered the lovers' nest. The spell was cruelly broken and Atilar was dragged to a prison cell. In shock he lay on the hard stones, unable to move day after day.

As Atilar studied the stagnant water which stood in the crevices of the cold stone floor, he thought back on his life. He had never been given any choices. From birth, he had been told what his destiny was. Trained relentlessly all through childhood, he had never played. He had never loved. He had become a master; but looking back, he saw the emptiness of it all. Something had always been missing, and until he saw his beloved, he had known no name for the hollow space within him which endless discipline and repetitious ritual could never fill. There had been no time or place for feeling, no spontaneity, no love, and it seemed clear to him now that ideals which are projected into form must inevitably become traps, as confining as the prison cell he lay in. He had faithfully carried out the covenants of the Order of the Blue Robes, never having been allowed to create anything for himself. In essence, he had been a slave.

Master Qi entered Atilar's cell. The two men looked at each other and tears formed in the eyes of Master Qi.

"My son, you have failed your final test. You have defiled a virgin of the Moon Goddess, and now you must die."

Atilar knew that Qi spoke only truth. Somewhere deep within his soul, Atilar knew that a life without feeling, without love, was a life barely lived, and so he accepted his fate. He was ready to die.

Because Master Qi had begged for leniency, Atilar would lose only his life and be spared the ultimate horror. The laser beam emitted from the central crystal would destroy his physical body, but his soul would remain intact. Atilar nodded in understanding; he must face death by execution. He had left his body many times before, but this time he would not return.

The guards came to the cell and escorted Atilar to the chamber of death, where he was chained to a wall in front of the huge crystal. Everyone left the room. The beam was turned on and, in seconds, the body of Atilar changed to nothing more than ash.

As Atilar floated free of his disintegrating flesh, his love for the young priestess drew him to her quarters. Her beautiful deep blue eyes were red and swollen from crying, and Atilar could see that the girl was with child. He wanted so desperately to hold her once more, to care for her. It was so sad. My innocent darling, he thought, what will become of you? The pain in his heart at leaving her was more than any man could endure. How would he ever find her again?

Gracie was exhausted. She was crying for Atilar and the girl, and that laser thing scared her half to death. Why couldn't she have just been beautiful, rich, and powerful like other normal people who remembered their past lives? Holy Moley! It certainly hadn't been easy out there.

# VIII

# CHANDHROMA

Inanna and Melinar moved into Gracie's consciousness, and Olnwynn followed them. From Gracie's point of view, they appeared as a subtle golden force field containing three tall figures who stood in her living room near the fire. Gracie had been absorbing the lessons of Atilar's life data.

She sighed, "How can there be so much suffering? How can Prime Creator watch this endless drama of life and death, of beauty and pain. What *is* Prime Creator?"

Melinar answered her, "Prime Creator *IS*."

Oh, no! Not that one, Gracie thought. "Listen, mister, when your heart is broken, the concept of *IS* doesn't feel too comforting."

Inanna thought of some of her experiences on Earth. Even as an alien being from another time frequency, Inanna had felt her heart break more than once. She wished she could think of something to say to give Gracie the answer she required. Inanna turned to Melinar, imploring him to come up with something.

"My child, this is the task you face," he said. "You must jump from *The* 10,000 *Things*, across the abyss of your doubt, to the place of the great *IS*. There you will find the truth you seek by feeling what Prime Creator feels. There you will know."

That sounds pretty scary, Gracie thought. She figured *The* 10,000 *Things* must be all those petty thoughts and things that distract all humans every minute of the day, none of which seem to matter at all when one comes close to death, experiences a tragic loss, or faces any real turning point. But, that abyss idea filled her with fear. She thought of that movie with Harrison what's-his-name, when he stuck his foot out over a seemingly bottomless gorge to take a leap of faith. There had been an unseen bridge for him and he had just walked across. Would it be so easy for her? Gracie was afraid of heights. She had vertigo just standing on a balcony; her feet would tingle and she would feel pulled toward the edge.

Olnwynn saw an opening and introduced himself. With Inanna's help, he offered Gracie his protection and courage. Inanna ran Olnwynn's life data for Gracie while simultaneously running Gracie's for Olnwynn.

Inanna picked a moment of Gracie's childhood and slowed it down for Olnwynn. Gracie, barely three years old at the time, was seated at the dining room table with her family. Gracie's father handed her a piece of fried chicken that Gracie didn't want. Gracie lifted the drumstick and threw it with some force against the wall.

Olnwynn laughed, seeing his own stubbornness in Gracie, and then he recognized and knew who the members of Gracie's family were. "By the gods! It's them, all of them!" Olnwynn was amazed to realize that Gracie's mother was his pretty wife, her father was Olnwynn's brother, and Gracie's brother was none other than Olnwynn's son. They were all still together in another time! Why had Gracie been born into a family with these three who obviously still carried bad feelings and memories of him? Or was it Gracie they feared and resented? No wonder Gracie was not happy!

Inanna answered Olnwynn's thoughts, explaining that it was a most useful means of learning and evolving. And besides, those three wanted to be together. They shared a bond. As Olnwynn, you controlled and brutalized them. Now as Gracie, the experience is quite different; reversed, in a way.

Gracie, who couldn't help listening, was thinking: If Inanna wanted to experience these things, why didn't she just get in a body *herself* and live, instead of making Gracie and Olnwynn do it?

"I did, Gracie. I *am* you. I have been everything you have been, and have felt everything you have felt." Inanna hoped to make her understand, but it just didn't look that way from where Gracie was standing in a physical body, the vulnerable flesh and blood with a half-wired nervous system.

"It is that half-wired nervous system I hope to correct," Inanna continued. "If all my multidimensional selves gather enough data to perceive the repeating patterns of their life experiences, perhaps one, perhaps you, Gracie, will expand yourself beyond your limitations and activate the divine genetic codes latent within you. It is possible. It would be as if you added a greater capacity to your computer. You have the technology; you only lack the *will* to do so. There are so many distractions, *The* 10,000 *Things*, and the electro-magnetic frequency grid that has been placed around your planet by those who wish you to remain as slaves."

Gracie was beginning to get some feeling for what Inanna was saying. If she, Gracie (who was, it seemed, Inanna), could somehow merge with Olnwynn and Atilar, as well as all the others who were in actuality also Gracie, then there was a chance that so much combined data and knowledge would trigger the dormant genes. Would the change in one human be passed on to the others?

"Yes!" Inanna replied, sighing with a sense of satisfaction that she had gotten through to at least one of her multidimensional selves. At this Olnwynn perked up and began to laugh.

"This could be fun!" he said. Promising to help Gracie to find the necessary courage, Olnwynn went over and sat down by the dogs, wishing he could pet them. Gracie noticed that both dogs were calm in the presence of her new friends. Well, she certainly wasn't alone anymore!

"Who else is there?" she asked Inanna and Melinar.

Chandhroma had never been truly beautiful as her mother was, but she was pretty and graceful. She was lucky not to have been suffocated at birth as was the custom for many female babies in those times. Her mother could not bear to kill the child, even though there was no reason to keep her.

The time was the sixteenth century AD in northern India. Chandhroma's mother was a prostitute, albeit a very high-class courtesan, who had fallen in love with a powerful advisor to the Sultan of Kashmir. Chandhroma's mother was only useful to this man as a mistress, not as the mother of his children. Of course, if the child had been a son, some place would have been found for him at the court. But the daughter of a prostitute was of no use to anyone. So, at the age of three, Chandhroma was given away to the school of dancing. There she was brought up to be a court dancer and had gone through a rigorous training. Fortunately, Chandhroma excelled at this art because she passionately loved to dance.

Chandhroma sat alone in the Temple of Dance. She came here often late in the night to dance for "the lady" who sometimes appeared to her. Surrounding her were stone columns with fantastic carvings of Kali and Laksmi, the Gandharvas, the apsarases, and dancing dakini. A single candle in front of her lit the shadows of the great hall, and a full moon drenched the polished marble floors with cool light.

Chandhroma sat in absolute stillness. She was fourteen years old and had been trained in the arts of dance for eleven years. She missed her mother, but "the lady" who came to her filled the emptiness in her heart and seemed like a goddess to Chandhroma. Like Krishna, her lady had lovely turquoise blue skin. She wore many necklaces of lapis lazuli and golden bracelets, and Chandhroma thought her blue lady was even more beautiful than her own mother.

Chandhroma gently rose and began to dance, gracefully turning and spinning while the tiny silver bells on her ankles echoed soft tones through the columns in the hall. In her mind, Chandhroma became one with the goddess. Images of the blue lady, of Lakshmi and Tara filled her awareness. She called the dancing dakinis into her body and became one with the moonlight. Her hands were graceful expressions of human hope and her body sang with the beauty of the night. Dancing alone for her goddess was

Chandhroma's greatest joy.

Sensing the presence of the blue lady, Chandhroma ceased the dance and became still. Her breath was short, moving her breasts almost imperceptibly. She called out, "Lady, I hoped this evening to speak with you. Soon I will be taken into the Palace of the Sultan to dance. Will you be with me to guide my dance?"

Inanna answered her, "Yes, my beloved girl, I am always with you wherever you go. I am a part of you. My love for you is eternal and you are never truly alone, for I am here watching over you. I love that which you are."

Chandhroma felt the presence of an intruder. "Who is there?" she cried out.

"Only an admirer, my child," the stranger spoke. "I am Vasudeva, the architect of the Sultan's palaces. Your dance teacher has told me of your nocturnal performances, and I have come here in secret to gaze upon your beauty. I am an old man, and I mean you no harm. I want to be your friend."

Chandhroma sought the approval of her blue lady, who smiled and nodded her head. Then this is my destiny, Chandhroma thought.

Vasudeva continued, "I understand that you thirst for knowledge, and that you spend your free time drawing the temple sculptures and pavilions. I wish to teach you these things. I once had a lovely daughter such as you, but at the peak of her beauty, she was taken from me by a mysterious illness. She was my only light in this world, and you remind me of her. Let me become your mentor when you move into the palace, and I will teach you to read and write. I will teach you mathematics, language, and architecture."

It was unheard of. No woman was allowed to learn such things. Chandhroma had always wanted knowledge and had secretly attempted to learn to write Sanskrit, but women were not encouraged in such matters; Chandhroma was nothing more than a temple dancer. Her status was not much better than a prostitute, like her mother.

"And what will I have to do in return?" she asked.

"Work very hard. You must apply yourself to these new arts and continue your dance. Otherwise, you would not be allowed to remain in the palace. You are in the service of the Sultan, but he is my friend, and he is enjoying this little folly of mine. It is well known that you are gifted, that the gods smile on you and take a special interest in you. I intend to do the same. You will be like a daughter to me."

"I accept." It was all she could say, her heart being in her throat. Surely her blue lady must have brought this opportunity to Chandhroma. Truly, it must be a gift from the gods.

Inanna was very pleased with Chandhroma's progress. The girl had a wonderful mind. She learned quickly, and became Vasudeva's greatest pride. Chandhroma's reputation as a dancer in the palace grew. At the same time, she assisted Vasudeva in his architectural projects, and was even commissioned to design a small garden. Kashmir was world-famous for its gardens. It was a wonderful time for Chandhroma. Vasudeva loved her, and while she was admired and courted by many, only dance, knowledge and learning were of any importance to her. She thought there must be other women who desired such opportunities.

One day, Chandhroma was alone drawing in the garden she had designed. A handsome young man appeared before her and introduced himself. He was the Sultan's son and heir. Chandhroma naturally had seen him at the court when she had danced, but she had never dreamed of meeting him, certainly not alone. The Sultan had named his son Arjuna after the famous archer in the ancient scriptures.

"Chandhroma, I have fallen hopelessly in love with you," Arjuna declared. "I have watched you dance, and Vasudeva has told me many stories of your grace and cleverness. Was there ever a woman in my father's kingdom as gifted and lovely as you?"

Their eyes met for a time in silence. The girl had not thought much about romance; she did not have the time for such pursuits, and she did not want to end up a prostitute like her mother. But this young man, this Arjuna, was bringing feelings into her being that she had not known existed.

Arjuna then began to speak sweetly in a spontaneous expression of his love and desire for her:

"Chandhroma, I have been waiting for this moment.
Come to me my beloved, let my arms
embrace you.
Your radiant skin conceals the fires burning
beneath it.
Every cell of my body resonates with your being.
I long to be close to you, Beloved.
Your eyes draw me closer to my Home.
I follow their deep darkness like an innocent child
who knows only one calling.
Drawn to you like the Tides by the Moon,
flames spread across my body.
Desire overwhelms me on these summer afternoons.
I envision every aspect of your being.
Separate in body, united in soul and spirit,
you are ever with me.
I feel your heartbeat, your touch, your breath.
My cells vibrate with your life and my longing

for our Union.
How I have longed for one such as you in All Times
    and Places.
I seek the warmth of your gentle kiss to awaken the
    true fires burning within me.
Let my love, as sunlight, spill over your body
    and soul."

Chandhroma remained transfixed by his words; her heart was captured. She smiled as Arjuna sat down close to her and touched her hands. At last, the two began to laugh softly and speak as if they had known each other all their lives, and beyond. It is said true love can be that way.

Inanna was very happy for Chandhroma, but she also sensed danger. Already there were many gossiping women in the Sultan's court who had come to envy and despise the girl. Now that the son of the Sultan had turned his affections to her, who knew where their jealousies might lead. Poison was the common solution for rivalry in the harem.

Women in the palace were allowed so little freedom that their energies frequently unleashed themselves on each other. Occasionally, a male baby would even be killed to remove a potential heir. The harem could be a dangerous place. As a dancer, Chandhroma had not really been a part of that world, and she had enjoyed the protection of Vasudeva. But the attentions of Arjuna would make her a target for a frustrated mistress with ambitions of power. Inanna knew that the women of that time knowingly conspired against each other to defend what little territory they possessed. The powerlessness of women hurt Inanna deeply, but it was imperative that she warn Chandhroma.

Chandhroma, however, had fallen in love and was in a faraway world under Arjuna's spell. The two lovers spent their days drinking wine and making love in the magical gardens of Kashmir. Everyone in the palace was discussing their liaison. Try as she might, Inanna could not get Chandhroma's attention. How could she warn the girl?

One day Chandhroma returned to her room and found a gift on her table. It was a golden bottle with blood-red rubies encrusted upon it. The skill of its creator was impressive, and there was a note describing the magical properties of the contents. It was said to be an elixir for eternal beauty and vitality. Innocently, Chandhroma opened the vile and smelled its contents. The scent of a hundred roses filled the room, and Chandhroma was overcome with a desire to taste the elixir. Fearing the worst, Inanna summoned her powers and knocked over a beautiful fragile vase to get Chandhroma's attention. Spilling water, the vase clattered, breaking on the marble tiles, but Chandhroma was oblivious, possessed by the spell of the fragrance of roses.

Chandhroma lifted the bottle to her lips. The very moment Chandhroma tasted the liquid, she felt a violent contracting in her body. As she fell to the hard floor, she thought of Arjuna. How she longed to feel his arms around her, to once more taste his lips and gaze into his eyes. She tried to call out, but all her strength was gone. Her life slipped away from her.

As Chandhroma rose up out of her body, Inanna was there to embrace her.

# IX

# BOOKS AND SHOES

Gracie remembered how she had loved to dance. As a little girl, while lying in her bed, she would take large scarves under the covers and pretend they were her dancing costume, all the while imagining that she was a famous dancer in a magic kingdom. Her imagination would allow her to live such flights of fancy for hours. She had studied ballet for seven years, and her mother bought her a pair of red toe shoes because Gracie had so loved the movie *The Red Shoes*. Gracie thought of the shoes she had lost that day in the city. It seemed so long ago.

Gracie wondered if Chandhroma's life as a dancer had somehow influenced Gracie to love dance? Did all the multidimensional lives bleed through to all the others in some way? Gracie tried to picture herself wielding an axe, and Olnwynn laughed out loud. He had attached himself to

Gracie's consciousness, as he was most interested in Gracie's family and he was very fond of her dogs. He ran with them in the forest, teasing them by passing through trees.

The memories of the other selves were so vivid. For Gracie, it was as if she were being shown holographic full-color movies of the lives of people she felt mysteriously close to. Gracie thought of the many magical occurrences in her life. She knew she had inherited her psychic abilities from her mother, who had always known what Gracie was thinking—a source of discomfort for Gracie because her mother rarely approved of her.

In the sixties, Gracie had experimented with mind-altering substances like so many others of her generation, but a voice within her had warned her to stop; Gracie could not attribute her longing to know truth to any of those experiences. She had been intent on finding answers from adolescence on, and had kept a journal since the age of four-teen. The journal had begun with the words: "This is to prove that a young girl can think for herself." It was think-ing for herself that had always gotten her in trouble.

No one wanted Gracie to do anything but look pretty and marry a suitably wealthy man. Her mother warned Gracie that no one would ever marry her if she kept reading all those books! Gracie found her life empty and filled with hypocrisy. She tried to be like everyone else, but she just could not. It was as if a pied piper were playing somewhere inside her, calling her to another sort of life. Why had she ever been born into her family? Now, it seemed as though Olnwynn had the answers for her. Her mother, in fact, owed her the life she had taken from Olnwynn, but her poor mother wasn't happy either. Was the past haunting her mother and father also? Was not her father as great a tyrant as Olnwynn had been? When would it ever end?

"It will only end when you change it," Inanna said. "The key is within you, Gracie. Your realizations, coupled with all the wisdom of the other multidimensional selves, will activate the dormant hormonal secretions in your body. Your consciousness will transform your physical body, and as your perception of reality changes, so will life on this plane. But, I cannot do it for you, Beloved, you must do it for yourself. It is a free-will Universe, and if I make you change, I break the law of free will."

Gracie thought that was too bad. She would love to have Inanna and Melinar touch her with a magic wand and change everything in the world. But, apparently, that was not to be. Somehow, Gracie had to do this thing for herself. She thought of all the stories she had read about great masters who had spent years disciplining themselves high on the tops of mountains. In the famous Hindu epic, *The Mahabharata*, people who aspired for truth or assistance from the gods would always perform what was called *tapas*. Gracie had learned that meant "generating heat." Something could actually be produced in the body which was like a *divine heat*, and she wondered if that was the secret to activating the endocrine system? It was written that in ancient times, people who wanted to attain magical abilities would stand around on one toe for 2,000 years, an image which always amused Gracie. She tried to imagine herself balancing on one toe for even five minutes!

Gracie had sought out many teachers and schools to answer her endless questions, but each source of knowledge had fallen into the trap of being seduced by the power they wielded over their students. At first, this was very painful to Gracie. But as she saw the pattern repeat itself, she learned that veiled tyranny was the logical conclusion of most schools. Spontaneous truth could never be put into law. The best expression of this she had found in the Chinese master, Lao Tzu who said something about truth being unspeakable except by those who did not understand it.

Gracie knew that she must find truth within herself.

Atilar was beginning to get used to his new surroundings. He had been trained to leave his body and travel to other dimensions, so death was not much of a shock for him. But the loss of his true love, the young priestess of the Moon, had temporarily damaged his perceptions. The passion they had produced together had changed Atilar's normal energy level drastically, and he had required some time to assimilate these changes.

Instinctively, Atilar knew who and what Melinar and Inanna were. He easily absorbed the life data of the other multidimensional selves. Atilar recalled that he had once visited Olnwynn on the battlefield. Atilar had been attracted by the intense psychic heat Olnwynn generated in these moments. Olnwynn became one with his axe as he chopped his enemies down; no one escaped his focused will. At such times, Olnwynn's frequency was identical to Atilar's when he tuned the crystals.

Atilar offered his consciousness and his life data to Gracie. Gracie opened herself to Atilar's field of energy and felt her entire body change. She felt lighter and stronger. Atilar had much to offer and much to teach. At night, snuggled in her bed, Gracie assimilated the experiences of her multidimensional selves. In her mind, she embraced them, feeling so much love for each and every one of these beings. No matter what they had done, she could not bring herself to judge them. They were simply who they were, and she loved them. Perhaps, she thought, this is how Prime Creator feels about all creation.

As time had passed on Earth, the men on the planet had become more and more afraid of their feelings. This was a natural consequence of constantly being sent off to useless wars where they were often killed or maimed. Many men had experienced being wounded and lying helplessly on the battlefield for days as they prayed death would take them before vultures could tear them apart. They were indoctrinated not to show their feelings, not to act like women. They were told that women were inferior. In exchange for a feeling of superiority, men had cut themselves off from experiencing their own tenderness and emotions. Merwin, another of Inanna's selves, was one such man.

Merwin grew up watching his father abuse his mother. His mother was a sensitive and intelligent woman who taught Merwin to read and to love books. She impressed on him that knowledge was the only thing of real value in life. Merwin tried to defend his mother, but he was only a small boy. One day in a fit of rage, his father accidentally killed his mother. Desperate and miserable, Merwin ran away.

In Alexandria, there was said to be a great library filled with books and learning from all over the world. Merwin dreamed that he would be happy for the rest of his days just living in such a place. Dirty and hungry, he arrived at the library gate. Merwin begged the custodian to let him do chores; he would do anything to stay in this place. Taking pity on this little lost boy, the custodian let him in.

For rest of his life, Merwin chose to stay in the great library. He read and catalogued everything. He occasionally thought of his mother, how she would have been pleased that he lived in a such a place. But it was too painful to think about her for long. He became a legend in Alexandria, and a joke. Everyone admired him for his knowledge, and it was Merwin they went to when they wanted to find this or that book or scroll. But they also laughed at him, saying he was as dried-up as his ancient scrolls. It was well known that he had no life beyond his beloved books. Merwin was never with a woman. A recluse living in the midst of fading papyrus and dusty shelves, he never even left the library.

One day, hundreds of soldiers came to Alexandria. They conquered the city and set fire to the library. It was said the flames from the burning library could be seen for miles. All of the stored knowledge of antiquity went up in those flames. The histories of Atlantis, Lemuria, and count-less other ancient civilizations were turned to ash. Merwin stayed there that day. Where could he have gone? Without his library, Merwin did not want to live.

And so Merwin joined Melinar and Inanna in the oval with the others. Merwin, who since the death of his mother had never allowed himself to feel, shed tears of transparent ether in a strange dimension.

# X

# THE WORLD
# OF APPEARANCES

Melinar infused his consciousness into the collection of beings gathered in Inanna's oval: Atilar, Chandhroma, Olnwynn, Gracie's awareness, Merwin, and, of course, Inanna. As Melinar began to speak, the colorful geometric forms, the brilliants, began to mutate rapidly.

"No aspect of Prime Creator is really separate from the rest. The door of release from the world of appearances can take any form. Each life expression carries the potential of freedom, and each of you clothed yourself with the colors and tempcraments available to you in the time you lived within. Because of the power of the five senses, you became lost in the duality of these expressions and allowed yourselves to be carried along by the inevitable unceasing polarities. But, as you can see, those realities have vanished except as stored data. You exist separately and yet, you are eternally connected to all. Nothing ever dies, and nothing is ever lost.

"In one dimension of reality, none of us has ever left the mind of Prime Creator."

Gracie sat in the cedar forest with her beautiful dogs, thinking how sad most of her lives had been. All that struggle to learn and become something, only to be lost in some senseless impulse. What was it all for? If only she could go back and heal the others. If Merwin's father had been gentle, if Chandhroma had only listened to Inanna and not drunk the poison, if Atilar had stopped at gazing into the eyes of his young priestess, if Olnwynn hadn't loved to drink. If only! It was the ongoing story of the human species. War and destruction were ominous enough in the history books, but when you lived them personally, the pain was intimate and pervasive.

Gracie was beginning to adjust to this barrage of information. The stories of her other lives fascinated and exhausted her. She noticed that most of her death experiences were not easy; perhaps death was not meant to be easy. Perhaps it is the only way we can be persuaded to leave our bodies. Somehow she was gaining a little detachment from all the data, and was beginning to see all the lives as parts of a puzzle that moved in cycles. There were more than a few repeating patterns. She felt as though she were a private detective on the verge of solving a great mystery. But would it ever be solved? Was it even *meant* to be solved?

Gracie lay on the hard forest floor and breathed deeply. The scent of cedar filled her, and she closed her eyes.

Sky Maiden lay on the floor of the tepee. The Medicine Man had tied her to the ground to "tie down the pain." Sky Maiden knew that was nonsense. She knew she was dying. What did men know about having babies? Her baby was turned around and jammed up in her body. The pain increased as she lost more and more blood. Where was Little Cloud, her friend and midwife?

Did Little Cloud want Flame Feather so much that she would let her friend, Sky Maiden, die in childbirth? Sky Maiden thought of Flame Feather, her husband. They had always loved each other. They had been together all their lives; even as children they had been inseparable. And, of course, Little Cloud had followed them whenever she could. Sky Maiden could understand how Little Cloud would love Flame Feather, but she had not minded because she never doubted Flame Feather's love for her. He belonged to Sky Maiden and no other.

Long before the white men came to their lands, the members of Sky Maiden's tribe lived peacefully in their beautiful hills. They respected the Earth and all the spirits. These people worked to achieve harmony with the wind and the stars, and they knew how to become one with all the animal spirits. Sky Maiden had been initiated as a little girl in the knowledge of the night skies. Spending long hours in silence under the stars, she would bring the essences of the sky into the tribe and its lands. Sky Maiden's wisdom was revered.

Her tribespeople believed that they had come from the stars and that one day they would return. The cluster of seven stars which they called the Sisters was known to be their origin. On many dark nights, Sky Maiden had gazed up at that cluster as she spoke to the Blue Lady who often appeared to her. The Lady gave her insights into the ways of wisdom, and encouraged her to honor herself. Sky Maiden had come to love this Blue Lady, and to believe that someday the tribe would return to the heavens and to the stars.

Flame Feather was a strong and handsome young man who adored his Sky Maiden. They had spent many hours together, laughing and walking through the forest, or riding across the hills on horseback with the wind in their souls. Life was sweet when they were together. In marriage, they had already given birth to a baby boy. Why was this second birth causing such difficulty?

The pain became excruciating; she had lost too much blood. Sky Maiden pulled against the leather ties as the sweat trickled down her face. If only she could get free. She stared up at the opening in the top of the tepee where she could see a small bit of blue sky. Why had they left her alone? A searing pain tore through her exhausted body, and then she felt nothing more. Sky Maiden rose up out of her tethered body; looking down, she saw her blood everywhere.

Little Cloud entered the tepee and cried out to find her friend dead. Pulling the baby from Sky Maiden's still-warm body, Little Cloud cut the umbilical chord and slapped the babe's bottom hard. A little baby girl began to shriek; still covered in blood, she was alive.

Flame Feather and the others entered. Sky Maiden felt her husband's shock and pain at the sight of her limp body. She knew he would not cry, he could not, it was not their way. But something inside him broke, and he would never be himself again. For those who are destined to be together, when that togetherness is finished, all of life is finished. Flame Feather would not hold the child.

Little Cloud did not know if her jealousy had kept her from the birthing for so long. Why had she not returned as she had promised? She began to clean the blood from the child's body. Little Cloud knew that Flame Feather would never be hers; he was among the walking dead now, no use to anyone. She would take the child and raise her. At least she would have his child.

The baby could easily see Sky Maiden's etheric body, though no one else could. "Mommy, why are you leaving?" The thoughts of mother and child were as one. Still hovering above, Sky Maiden spoke to her baby. "My little one, my sweet child, you must be brave. Know that I love you. Comfort your father if you can, and stay with Little Cloud. She is sworn to care for you now, and you are all she will ever have of him. I am sorry I cannot be with you to teach you the ways of the sky. Farewell, my little daughter, my love is always with you."

Years later, a thin scruffy Indian girl tagged along after her father. The man, aged beyond his years, his body stiff with grief, ignored her. The small girl had dressed herself in boys' clothing, hoping to please her father. She pulled at the old warrior's sleeve, but he not notice her. For him, she did not even exist.

Gracie was crying. Oh, my god, she thought, that poor little girl! Life was made up of endless textures of experience. Who but a being of infinite and limitless power would dare to place itself in such a precarious world as this.

Gracie thought about never having wanted children. She had told herself it was because she was afraid she might treat her children as her parents had treated her. But deep within her there was also a hidden fear of the act of child-birth itself. Was Sky Maiden's life imprinted on Gracie's instincts?

And Flame Feather reminded Gracie of her childhood sweetheart, Michael. They had met when Gracie was only twelve, but they had both immediately known they belonged together. Michael had planned to marry Gracie, but as the years went by, her fear of being like her mother had pushed Gracie further away from him. She talked of leaving, of flying off to New York or Paris. He had married someone else, a friend, someone who felt like Little Cloud to Gracie.

Gracie imagined herself to be walking in an endless maze where she kept stumbling on parts of herself she had not known existed. Somehow all of the parts were connected, somehow all the connections could answer Gracie's questions and fill the emptiness she had always felt inside of her.

Gracie saw the familiar beautiful geometric forms in the Eye of her Mind. The colors were rich, and the sparkling forms moved in rapid succession as Melinar began to speak.

"All the systems of philosophy and religion available in printed form are reflections of the Truth at various moments necessary to fulfill the needs of that time. It is not necessary to attach your consciousness to any of these systems, and the forms of religious expression that exist are still useful for many, but countless more forms were lost from the pre-historical period because nothing was written down. Truth is truth in any present moment of existence, regardless of the form it manifests. The form is subject to the needs and capacity for reception of the existing race of beings as determined by the point of their evolution. Those thought formations/constructions which we build around us to protect us are often the very same forms which invite our demise. Prime Creator is ever in motion and changing."

Melinar's brilliants were moving faster than Gracie's human eyes could follow, but she understood that there was some ineluctable trap in the human need to stop change. Whatever was set into stone would inevitably be worn away. What we tried to hold onto would be lost. No one could stop the river.

Gracie got up and went to lie down next to her dogs. Snuggling into their thick black fur, she imagined herself safely nestled in the arms of Inanna. The beautiful blue goddess embraced little Gracie, and Gracie fell fast asleep. It was good to be home.

# XI

# THE CURTAIN

Inanna and Melinar scanned their consciousness for Atilar. He was so adept at projecting himself into other realities, it was difficult to keep track of him. He kept wandering off to be with the people who appeared out of liquid—the Liquidians, as he chose to call them. Atilar was fascinated by their fluid state, and they were equally interested in his knowledge of the hard objects, crystals.

Inanna was becoming more and more concerned with the progress of her multidimensional selves. She knew that in the year 2011 the contractual agreement between the Inter-Galactic Council and Marduk, the Pleiadian tyrant, would come to its completion. The Earth would begin to separate itself into at least two realities, and only those humans who had mastered the fourth and fifth dimensions would have the ability to leave the tyrannical frequencies of

Inanna's distant cousin, the reptilian master himself, Marduk.

If only her family had let him die when she had succeeded in burying him in the Pyramid at Giza. Ever since that day, Marduk had carried his hatred of Inanna across the planet Earth, and had purposely sought to enslave and degrade women, especially the priestesses of her temples for the knowledge they had taught. For the last few thousand years, Earth had been a sad reminder of the degradation of the goddess and her wisdom.

One of Inanna's multidimensional selves had been a lovely young girl who lived in Spain during the Inquisition. This girl's name was Rachael, and she was born into the Jewish faith. Inanna had thought she was being careful; she only gave Rachael healing powers. It was not as if the girl was so powerful she would pose a threat or foment rebellion. No, Rachael was just a simple, uneducated, sweet girl whose touch and manner sometimes brought relief to the sick. But that was cause enough for the Inquisition to accuse Rachael of being a witch, a servant of the Devil. She was dragged off to prison and brutally tortured before being burned at the stake.

When Gracie was shown Rachael's life data, she had begged not to see what had been done to Rachael. Her tormentors had become obsessed with their own demons while they tortured this innocent girl. Finally, Rachael was dressed in white to signify that they had purified her, and then led to the stake. As the fires were lit under her, three angels came and lifted Rachael from her wracked body, and freed her from the pain of being burned alive. Many women on planet Earth experienced this; residual fears remain deep within their cellular memory. Fleeting visions of such moments haunted Gracie.

Inanna knew that all of her selves would have to contribute to Gracie's transformation. She wanted Gracie to embody the wisdom and knowledge from all the others, male and female. Inanna called to Atilar, who was giving the Liquidians a dissertation on crystals.

"I, Atilar, am a Keeper of the Crystals. I serve the Light and communicate with the Guardians of Evolution." Atilar now knew that those guardians were Inanna and Melinar.

Atilar continued speaking to the Liquidians. "In the time of my existence, the central concept of worship was light—not a person, god, or object. Light is found in every part of existence. Inner light, as well as outer reflected light, was perceived as the heart of life and worshipped as such.

"The crystals symbolize many things. They relate to light in various waves, obvious and subtle. They are response systems to light, heat, and energy. Like small computers, crystals can be used to store information, but they may also be programmed on a more subtle, psychic level. Their natural proclivity for a harmonious atomic structure allows them to suggest and transmit various states of consciousness, such as creativity and healing, through harmony, polarity, and energy.

"Crystals may also represent experiences as stored memory, and thus have the power to invoke the visual memory of these experiences. It is only the variable of quality and form of these experiences that allows the infinite levels of differences. All is truth. Each expression carries the light within."

Inanna interrupted. "Atilar, the Guardians of Evolution summon you to the central focal point."

Atilar apologized profusely to his new friends. He was certainly anxious to learn more about the Liquidians and how he might experience becoming a liquid. He bade them a fond farewell, and projected himself in thought toward the direction of the sonorous voice of Inanna.

"I am happy to be in your presence once again, beautiful Lady. Where is the one called Melinar? His geometric forms remind me of my crystals." Atilar found Melinar, who was beginning to mutate rapidly, as was his habit when he became excited. Melinar bonded his conscious awareness to Atilar. Gracie was still asleep, but in her dream state she sat in rapt attention while all of Inanna's selves coalesced into one awareness.

Melinar began to speak, his brilliants zooming. "Prime Creator is the Source of all Life. The Creator's fire is the liquid that runs through all beings and energizes them. While no experience is without some value, remembering and experiencing reunion with Prime Creator must ultimately come from within. Experiences in the time/space continuum and on the material plane will tie one to the *cause and effect* chain of such experience. Prime Creator is the within, and does not depend on any external forms or structures, which are Prime Creator also. The being who knows this truth is set free—for who, or even what, can own you when you know that the source of all is within you?

"The laws that govern the bonding of energy are correct and useful in the material realms. The atom is held together by the laws of polarity: the positive electrical charge of the proton, the neutral charge of the neutron, and the negative charge of the electron. In the realms of biology, polarities such as life and death, beginnings and endings, translate into limitation, contraction, and ultimately the illusion of death. In psychological terms, the laws of materialization give rise to the ego. The ego is a fictitious identity with a sense of fear, vulnerability, and a need to protect and defend itself. The moment the personality/ego identifies with any thought structure, it seeks to maintain that identity as a rock seeks to remain a rock.

"In order to maintain its identity with the chosen thought structure, it immediately begins to define its identification in relation to the identifications of other egos. Thus, it begins to produce endless systems of judgments to support such fictitious identities. As the personality continues in its definitions, it forgets its true nature, and begins to live in the fear of losing the fictitious identity it never really had. Thus, Prime Creator plays hide-and-seek with itself."

Melinar was capable of speaking in this manner for what might be perceived as an endless amount of Earth time. But to him such expression was sheer joy, and his brilliants never seemed to tire.

"Reality, as the personality perceives it from the self-imposed limitations of the five-sense-based hologram, is merely point of view. Each projection of Prime Creator takes on the veils of illusion and pretends to be separate from the others in order to collect data.

"Time and space allow Prime Creator expression in the infinite layers of dimensional realities. The secret of life is knowing that everything and everyone is eternally held by Love in the mind of God."

On waking from her dreams, Gracie remembered a poem she had read years earlier that had always stayed in her mind. Normally, she could never recall verse, but this poem had always remained close to her heart. The lines were written by a Sufi Master, Mahmud Shabistari, in the fourteenth century AD.

The poem spoke of the beauty of the face of the

beloved which remains present beneath the curtain of each atom.

Gracie had always imagined herself lifting the curtain from an atom, and there it would be, that illusive *something* she had longed for all of her life. The healing beauty of the face of the beloved would make her whole again, and she would remember. Gracie felt as if that time were getting closer. Since coming to the mountain, she had felt so different, as if her whole body were bubbling and changing, as if she were mutating.

Being alone on Lost Mountain was helping Gracie to find her way home.

# XII

# FLYING IN TIBET

In the early-morning light, Gracie watched the steam rise from a fresh cup of delicious coffee. She sat in the window watching the light of dawn spread itself out over the soft, snow-covered Olympic Mountains.

It was all so pristine and beautiful. Gracie was learning to let the silence fill her; the only sounds were the fire crackling and occasionally her dogs barking at coyotes. Snow-covered mountains, the starry skies of night, thick cedar forests, the wildflowers which spread over her small valley; these experiences were new to Gracie's senses, and she loved every moment. In some ways, she thought, one can only experience nature when one is alone. Why then did she always need to tell someone what she had seen?

As Gracie sipped the hot coffee, she thought of what she was learning. She had waited so long for this to happen.

There were many teachers in her life, some wonderful and some not so wonderful. She thought of the Tibetan monk she had studied with years ago. He was way beyond her understanding then. He had once waved his arm through a table, as if there were nothing solid, to show the illusory nature of the material world. She hadn't really understood, but she had wanted to, and when she moved on, she left him an intricate drawing to thank him for his wisdom.

Later, she had entered an ashram. The teacher had grown up in India, and had lived in a famous ashram there. For awhile, Gracie was happy. It was wonderful to be with many others whose only desire was to understand the meaning of life, and who did not laugh at her for wanting such knowledge. In meditation, Gracie did occasionally experience the feeling of being at one with life, with creation. But soon she began to notice that her teacher was falling in love with his own power, and Gracie could no longer explain his eccentric behavior to herself.

One day, sitting in a hall with hundreds of other disciples, Gracie's inner voice, that small quiet knowingness she had come to trust over the years, told her to go home and never come back. It was a shock to Gracie, and it distressed her, but she went home.

There alone, she paced back and forth in her kitchen, trying to understand why her inner voice had told her to leave. She was confused, and she hated to leave her friends. The voice said to her loud and clear, "BOOTS!" Gracie was thoroughly puzzled. Boots? What did that mean? Then it all came back to her.

Gracie had gone to her summer camp when she was only seven years old. On the first day of camp, there was an initiation. Everyone gathered together, and the leader of the camp asked a riddle: "What is boots without shoes?" Gracie was terrified, so afraid she would not know the answer, and the other girls would think she was stupid and not like her. She slipped to the back of the crowd. The children repeated "Boots without shoes!" like a chant until almost all the little girls guessed the answer.

Finally, the answer came to her. The answer was, of course, "Boots!" Gracie laughed out loud. The riddle was too simple. Her voice was telling her it was her fear of not understanding that made it so difficult, and very simply, she could trust herself; her teachings could come from within her. Gracie had learned all she could from the ashram, and it was time for her to move on. She could trust her inner guidance, knowing she was a part of life, a part of Prime Creator. The answers were within her all along.

High on Lost Mountain, Gracie laughed again at "boots without shoes." Her guides were sometimes comical and even occasionally tricky, but deep within her heart, she knew she could trust them. She gazed at the Olympic Mountains. The sunlight was streaming down the mountainsides in purple, pink, and gold. Gracie thought of how she had always been afraid of heights.

Choje Tenzin came to the monastery in Tibet when he was only seven. His parents could not afford to keep him, the last of their nine children. He was tearful when they left him at the gate, but there was nothing to be done, and his father struck him when he tried to run after them. The monk who came to the gate led little Tenzin away to a hall where there were hundreds of other boys. The hall was noisy with chattering children, their bowls clinking on the stone floors. Tenzin was given a bowl of hot buttered tea and left to fend for himself.

The first years were terribly lonely for Tenzin; he was a frail and sensitive child. At home, his older sisters had spoiled him with what little they could, and had shown him a great deal of affection. He was so lonely, and the other boys made fun of his physical weakness, until it was discovered that Tenzin could draw. This particular monastery was devoted to producing Tantric paintings, and anyone who proved to have talent was soon given special respect. Tenzin was sent to the Master Teacher of painting to be trained in the techniques and rituals of Tibetan art.

The master art teacher, Lin Pao, was a man of great physical beauty and refinement. It was rumored in the monastery that Lin Pao came from a very wealthy and aristocratic family in China. Lin Pao came to Tibet to put his considerable talents to their greatest use, and was revered as the greatest painter of Tibetan Tantras.

Tenzin was not trained by Lin Pao in the beginning, but after many years of serving as an apprentice, he was allowed to study directly under the great master. Tenzin stood for hours watching the delicate and strong hands of Lin Pao skillfully execute line and color. Tenzin worshipped Lin Pao. In truth, Tenzin was deeply in love with his teacher. It was only natural that a lonely little boy might come to have such feelings for one so great as Lin Pao, but these feelings were forbidden and remained secret.

The fact that Tenzin was regarded as a talented artist did not exclude him from the rigorous disciplines of the monastery. The lessons of abstinence from food and warmth, the hours of remaining utterly motionless in meditative positions, and the martial arts were all a part of Tenzin's everyday life.

There was one disciplinary attainment that all of the

students worried about. A select group of novice monks were trained to concentrate their energies to such heightened intensity that they could defy gravity and learn to fly. The monks spent years perfecting such concentration, perched on the edge of the cliffs high above the monastery. Not only was Lin Pao a great artist, he also had this ability to fly from the cliffs and not perish. Tenzin was determined to learn in order to please Lin Pao.

It was said that the secret to the art of flying was an unbroken focus. Many monks spent years in preparation for their first attempt, and many fell to their deaths. It was believed that all returned to life; even if a monk failed, he could reincarnate, return to the monastery, and, in an unbroken line, persist in his endeavor of such mastery.

One cold and windy day, Tenzin and a few other brave souls were sitting high on the designated cliffs when Lin Pao joined them. Naturally, Tenzin wanted to impress Lin Pao. Calling forth his greatest concentration, he hastily decided to attempt flight. Tenzin stood up and focused all his will, but as he stepped from the precipice, the confusion that motivated Tenzin also distracted him from his concentration. He felt the suppressed love he harbored for Lin Pao dilute the power of his will, and Tenzin dropped from the precipice, falling hundreds of feet. His body smashed upon the rocks below.

As Tenzin's consciousness drifted above the broken shell that had been his body, he gazed longingly at his idol Lin Pao. Ashamed, Tenzin dared not even say good-bye.

To Gracie it seemed as if most of her lives had ended hopelessly, but Inanna and Melinar explained to her that each life was a gathering of experience and information. Gracie and all the others were the sum total of each other; they shared the knowledge and wisdom that each had acquired so painfully.

Inanna showed Gracie how Tenzin had contributed to her being. The wisdom of Tibet was one of the last strongholds of truth in Gracie's time. Something had always driven Gracie to seek the truth, and she had always longed to go to Tibet. She had even studied with a Tibetan monk. Gracie's instinctive affinity for Tibetan teachings and art had given her great insight, and had allowed her to free herself from the narrow limitations of her own cultural upbringing. Tenzin's skill in painting had come through to Gracie, and she had recognized Lin Pao miraculously in her greatest teacher at the art school she had attended in New York! Well, what if Gracie was left with the residue of a fear of heights? She could get over it.

Gracie couldn't help thinking it was easy for Inanna and Melinar to say she could get over it. As far as she could see, they weren't actually in physical bodies, even though they said they were. Gracie was still having trouble seeing where it was all leading. In the midst of all this learning, she occasionally felt the urge to numb herself by watching television or going shopping. But where could a girl shop on Lost Mountain?

Gracie went to her bookshelf. My goodness, there were a lot of books. The last time she moved, even the movers were dismayed by the sheer volume of her collection. Gracie's library was full of all sorts of oddities, from Tolstoy to Lao-Tzu, from economics to UFOs; all sorts of subjects found their way into the chaos of her library.

Gracie's eye fell on a book she had been given many years ago. The book had been written in 1949 when Gracie herself was only four years old. She had attempted to read it in 1969. In those days, she had worn her hair long, down to her waist, and her wardrobe had consisted of two T-shirts and a skirt from India made of cotton. It was an exciting time to be in New York City with so many other young people who all imagined that they could change the world. Gracie had struggled to understand this book, but at that time she had not experienced enough of life to grasp its meaning. Now as she held it in her hands, it seemed to be very clear what its author was saying.

The universe was a holographic dream projected as thought within the mind of God, and only our individual perceptions of relative and varying rhythmic frequencies made the world appear real. The author went on to talk about how it is possible to go beyond ordinary time, to go into the past or the future, and even to pass beyond apparent dimension.

Gracie understood that this was exactly what she was doing. She was her other selves in the time of their life data, and simultaneously, Inanna was all of them, including Gracie. Time didn't exist except as a thought which allowed existence to play itself out in space. Gracie had become aware of the secret reality of the apparent world and had escaped the laws that held her to the illusion of time.

Gracie thought if Prime Creator was all things, then Marduk must also be a part of the divine play, a part of Prime Creator. Melinar was extremely pleased that Gracie could entertain this thought. Melinar understood that as much as it was Inanna's role to battle with Marduk, it was also the destiny of Marduk to be exactly as he was, for Prime Creator was all of Its varying parts, moving in the flow of time to test Itself, to express and to experience, to play. As Gracie became more capable of interacting with her other multidimensional selves, the more data and wisdom she could assimilate, and the greater her chance of activating her body's divine DNA—the genetic codes that were lost so long ago.

As best he could, Melinar embraced Inanna. There was still much to do, but they were making progress.

# XIII

# LUNCH WITH MARDUK

Marduk sat in his private dining room on top of the tallest building in Hong Kong. He was about to have lunch with the head of all the communications networks of planet Earth. Marduk glanced at his suit, Saville Row of course, and his Italian shoes. Earth was amusing, he thought. His plan was working out better than even he had hoped. Next week was his usual meeting with the world bankers, and the following week, the world's political leaders.

The dining room was lined with rare sculpture and antique mirrors, and the walls were paneled with polished mahogany. The tall ceiling glowed with crystal and gold chandeliers which lit the fresco paintings Marduk had removed from Egyptian tombs. The table was perfectly set with solid-gold flatware and china from Paris, not that Marduk needed to impress anyone; he simply liked beautiful things. Over the centuries he had made it his business to become a connoisseur of everything Earth had to offer.

Behind Marduk, down on their knees, six exquisitely beautiful concubines waited, ready to serve him at a moment's notice. If Marduk happened to drop a crumb during lunch, one of the girls immediately removed it from the white tablecloth with a silver trowel. At the doors stood four bodyguards; two more were stationed on the other side of the doors. All were trained as ninjas, just for fun. Marduk enjoyed pretending he was a movie star. He loved a good violent movie with lots of gore and martial arts scenes. After all, it was his world. He could play any way he liked.

Soon there wouldn't be any more discussion about who had the right to control Earth. Marduk had taken it, might makes right, and the planet rightfully belonged to him. He had always been able to dominate his father, Enki. Marduk couldn't help it if his father was weak, and he truly enjoyed breaking his father's will, or anyone else's for that matter. It seemed to him that the world was filled with weaklings, waiting for him to dominate them. There were the pushovers who weren't much of a challenge, and then there was the majority, which required a little brainwashing propaganda. A few even had to be tortured, but, in the end, almost everyone gave in.

It was the business of programming further brainwashing propaganda that would be discussed at this lunch, and Marduk wanted to make it very clear to his guest, the president of his communications network, just who was running the show. Marduk enjoyed bullying those in his employ; it was entertainment for him. Lately he had been rather bored. The year 2011 was approaching all too slowly. He did want that Intergalactic Federation out of his way for good.

Marduk knew everything about his father, Enki's, and

that witch Inanna's attempts to wake up the human species. He knew that Enki and Inanna, plus a few other members of his Pleiadian family, had hoped to prove to the Federation Council that the humans could, through their own free will, activate the dormant genes and take their place as equals in this galaxy, not as slaves.

Marduk had carefully followed all the life data of the projected multidimensional selves. It hadn't taken much to foil their pitiful attempts to believe in themselves. If their own passions didn't destroy them, it was easy enough for Marduk to arrange their deaths through one of his agents. History, as he had shaped it, allowed for many convenient waves of hysteria, all perfectly designed to wipe out any original thought. As long as the human beings believed that they were powerless, they could be *entrained* to worship Marduk in all his disguises. Always looking outside of themselves for help and comfort, the human species remained weak and vulnerable to Marduk's ingenious enslavements.

His new communications network idea was the best he had come up with so far. Silently, Marduk congratulated himself. A vast web of electromagnetic signals bounced off the satellites in orbit around Earth and kept the frequencies of the entire planet in a very limited spectrum. It was almost impossible for any human brain to think beyond the survival frequency. All that was left was to program images of wealth and power beyond the reach of most mortals, and thus leave humanity in a state of frustration and fear. It was too easy; Marduk was becoming more than a little bored.

He glanced at himself in one of the antique Renaissance mirrors that lined the dining room walls. God, he was handsome, he thought. Over the centuries, he had perfected his beauty with an endless number of ever-improving surgical procedures, but he had purposely left that trace of cruelty he was so famous for. It gave him pleasure to watch the expressions of terror on his victims' faces as they timidly approached him.

The network president was announced as he entered the room. Monsieur Atherton Spleek bowed obsequiously to Marduk. "Master, may I sit down?" he inquired.

Atherton dreaded these meetings. Marduk was terrifying to look at, and something bizarre always occurred, leaving Atherton queasy for weeks after. It was odd: Marduk managed to appear so handsome and youthful at first glance, but when you really looked at him, you couldn't help but wonder if Marduk wasn't the Devil himself. Atherton quickly pushed such thoughts out of his head. After all, he didn't believe in such things; he only believed in power and the bottom line, all of which Marduk made possible.

Atherton had been born in the slums of Jakarta. Even as a child he had been ambitious, waiting outside the doors of the city's shiny tall buildings and begging the men in their dark suits to let him serve them. In those days, the oil business in Jakarta was the only business, and lonely Western businessmen all wanted the same thing—women. So, little Atherton became a go-between for the oilmen and the pimps of the city. It was a beginning. One of the girls had given him the name Atherton, and he had made up the name Spleek. He had gotten it wrong from a television program; he had meant Spock, but Atherton Spleek it was.

Marduk liked Atherton because he was totally controllable. In spite of the position Atherton had risen to in the world, inside he was empty and dried up, and he knew nothing but obedience to his master, Marduk. Atherton noticed the girls crawling around on their knees. A nice touch, he thought; I must arrange for this in my Paris offices.

"Tell me your news, Atherton," Marduk commanded.

Atherton took a sip of Russian vodka, his hand trembling ever so slightly. "Master, everything is falling into place. The cable networks are set to merge with the cellular telephone companies, and the fiber-optic networks are almost completed."

Marduk was constructing a new electromagnetic grid under the Earth to secure his control in case some fool Federation ship should shoot down his satellites. The famous Law of Non-Interference was supposed to be in effect, but how one interpreted that law was still being debated in Federation law schools across the galaxies. Marduk himself had broken the law countless times, and he didn't trust his father, Enki, or anyone else in the entire Federation. And of course there was his grandfather, Anu, and his uncle, Enlil. Marduk knew all too well they were both out for him; somewhere, his entire family was plotting against him.

When Marduk had taken over Earth, he had also taken the planet Nibiru. Nibiru had belonged to Anu, and Earth had been given to Anu's sons, Enki and Enlil. Marduk had surprised everyone by conquering the entire Pleiadian star system with his massive armies of clones, all designed to resemble him. For centuries, he had been creating his battalions of warrior clones on a secret planet. No one had known until it was too late to stop him. Now, there was no one left to stand against him, except for the Federation itself. As for this attempt to empower the earthlings on a genetic level, Marduk couldn't take seriously the idea that any of the enslaved humans would ever stand up to him. It was too ridiculous to even merit his consideration.

He did hate that witch Inanna, and recalled the day of his trial so long ago. The entire family of Anu had gathered to judge Marduk. He was accused of overstepping his bounds and murdering his own brother, Dumuzi, who happened to be married to that ambitious female, Inanna. Marduk knew that Inanna wanted to control Egypt and was manipulating her weakling husband to that end. It hadn't bothered Marduk in the least to have his brother slaughtered. But it had definitely bothered him when Inanna suggested that Marduk should be buried alive in the pyramid and the rest of the family went along with it.

Even now, Marduk could hear the hard sounds of the huge stones hit as they dropped into place, sealing him in his tomb. The pyramid was such an excellent preserver, it would take him forever to die of starvation and dehydration. The fury and anger of that experience had mutated Marduk's being. He would never be the same after that day. The fervent pleading of his wife and his mother had pushed his father, Enki, into making Inanna relent. Inanna had agreed to release Marduk, demanding that he apologize to her. To add insult to injury, Inanna ordered Marduk to make offerings in her temples! Later, Marduk relished destroying those temples and murdering the priestesses in them.

Marduk had won; over and over he had beaten Inanna. He had taken pleasure in the steady suppression and degradation of females all over the planet, and with the advent of mass electronic communication it had become even easier. Marduk gleefully thought of all the women on Earth sitting on sofas, glued to their televisions, hopelessly wanting to be as beautiful or as rich as the androids parading daily in front of them. Wanting what could never bring them happiness broke their spirits and drained the life force from them. It was all so satisfying for Marduk, all those pathetic soap operas, all those desperate souls. He loved it!

"Tell me, Atherton, have the plans for more home

shopping channels been completed?"

"Yes, Master. By the year 2006 half of all the programming will be totally dedicated to the consumption of material goods. People will be working harder and harder for less and less money, and they will want more and more things, things they can never afford."

"How delightful!" Marduk exclaimed. Occasionally he could not help but be thrilled by his own genius. "And how is the alteration of the perception of time progressing?"

"It is as you have commanded, Master. The humans have less and less time for everything. They have no time for their families, and their children are increasingly vulnerable to our brainwashing techniques. The children already want everything they see on the screen without having to work for it. And best of all, no one has any time to think or to ask questions."

Marduk calmly nodded his approval, then ordered Atherton to stand and move away from the table. Atherton trembled; a wave of nausea came over him. One of the bodyguards sauntered toward Atherton and aimed a plasma weapon directly at his lower body. A beam of energy instantly evaporated Atherton's legs, and he dropped to the floor in agony. Marduk laughed hysterically. "Now, Atherton, I don't want you to get any ideas about your own power. You are completely my slave. Don't ever forget it. I can have you killed and cloned in a New York minute. No one would be the wiser."

The doors of the dining room opened and a team of surgeons entered to take Atherton away to replace his vanished legs. Marduk was sure this weakling had gotten the message. Atherton made a pitiful attempt to bow as they wheeled him out.

Marduk called for lunch to be served. It was a shame

that Atherton wouldn't be able to stay for the delectable meal that had been prepared. Grinning, Marduk shoved an entire chocolate-covered, braised baby pheasant into his mouth, bones and all.

# XIV

# MISTER RIGHT

Inanna woke from a terrible dream; her guardian dragons stared protectively at her. She had dreamed she was covered in chocolate, and that nasty Marduk was considering taking a bite. Inanna shivered. She rose from her bed and called Melinar into her consciousness. Melinar hovered in the room emitting soothing frequencies until Inanna and her dragons were once again calm. It was good to have a friend in these times. Inanna poured herself some Arcturian brandy. It was a little early, but it felt right as it slid down her throat, warming her lovely blue body all over.

Today was the day that Inanna and Enki were to attend a meeting of the Intergalactic Federation. Inanna was excited, not only because of the importance of their mission; she also secretly hoped to meet the mysterious stranger she had seen at the last meeting. She looked at all the clothes hanging in her closet, wondering what to wear to attract such a man.

Inanna knew absolutely nothing about her stranger, only that she had never seen anyone like him. He possessed an air of strength and quiet dignity which served to enhance his physical beauty. There was no one in Inanna's family even remotely like him, not even Anu or Enlil. He was tall, with long straight silver hair and eyes as dark as the night sky, eyes that sparkled with humor. To Inanna, it seemed as though there were diamonds in those dark eyes, and she wanted to know more about this man.

She found herself remembering his hands. They were completely gentle, with long delicate fingers, and yet, they showed no trace of weakness. Inanna had thought, here was a man who was not owned or possessed by the ebbs and flow of life. He was deeply passionate, but his passions did not overwhelm him. His countenance told her that he saw the humor of life and its endless changes, that life itself delighted him and that he felt compassion for all beings, in whatever state of evolvement they found themselves. Inanna felt that this man knew he was a portion of all life, and because of such knowledge, loved life in all its infinite parts.

Inanna wondered if she had really changed enough for him to notice her this time. She thought he had not even looked at her at the last meeting, or had he? Inanna couldn't find a thing to wear. After fussing about and throwing more than one garment on the floor, she settled for something modest and tasteful, a rare phenomenon in Inanna's wardrobe.

Inanna could feel Enki approaching on his dragon, then quickly felt the presence of two others, Anu and Enlil. Enlil always made Inanna a little nervous. She imagined he judged her harshly and did not really approve of his little granddaughter. But she was always delighted to see Anu. Inanna's very name meant "beloved of Anu," and it had always been true that Anu adored his great-granddaughter.

"My sweet girl, I am so pleased to see you again!" Anu hugged Inanna as tears came to her eyes. "I am very proud of you for endeavoring so diligently to help the earthlings. We have all changed since the old days, have we not, my little one?"

"Anu, how have you been? Tell me your news." Inanna bowed graciously to Enlil and asked about her mother, Ningal, and her father, Nannar, the son of Enlil.

Enlil and Anu had been gathering their forces in exile in a nearby galaxy, watching with great interest the experiments of projecting multidimensional selves into the time/space continuum of planet Earth. Inanna and Enki were not the only family members engaged in this activity. The family had come to recognize the truth: this was their only hope of creating another reality in which the human species could be free from the tyranny of their family member, Marduk.

As of late, Anu and Enlil had joined the Etherians on their ships which were orbiting Earth, patiently waiting for transformation to take place in the DNA of the human species, and protecting the planet from Marduk's raiders and other pirating aliens. The Etherians had pledged to protect Earth in order to give the human species a chance to activate their latent genes, and to prove to the council that they had indeed passed the adolescent stage all races progress through, that they were ready to be responsible for themselves, and to take their place as equals in the universe.

It was a tall order, Inanna thought, especially with Marduk foiling every attempt the family made on the humans' behalf. Certainly Marduk had done everything he possibly could to frustrate her plans. So many of her incarnational selves had fallen into his traps and lost their way. Could it really be that little Gracie was Inanna's last hope? She didn't want to think about that for very long; it was too scary.

Inanna, Anu, Enki, and Enlil walked into the Time Portal and transported themselves to the Federation Hall. Melinar followed as part of Inanna's consciousness. It was just as Inanna had remembered it—an enormous vaulted ceiling that allowed a view of all the galaxies. The sight was breathtaking. The heavens are even more beautiful than my jewels, she mused; it would be fun to play with the stars. The Hall was crowded with the usual vast assortment of beings from all kinds of racial heritages. The Etherians entered, acknowledging Anu and his family. The meeting was about to begin.

From the corner of her eye, Inanna noticed *him* quietly entering the Hall alone. He was just as Inanna had remembered him. His beauty came from a sovereign source deep within him, and magnetized her whole being. He was everything she wanted to become, graceful and gentle, yet strong and knowing. Inanna sat up straight and tried not to be obvious. If only he would sit in a place where she could see him easily. Much to her delight, he stepped up onto the raised area with the Etherians and sat to one side. Inanna made herself slow her breath. Her heart was beating too quickly, but he was so wonderful.

A very tall, elegant Etherian stood and began to address the Hall in sounds which became intelligible in the minds of all the members regardless of their native language or dialect. The Council made it clear that it was continuing to enforce its Law of Non-Interference while closely following the activities of the family of Anu, Marduk's adventures in particular. As of now, not much had changed. The end of the year 2011 was still the agreed-upon date to settle the matter of dominion on planet Earth. If enough of the human species could be convinced of the latent genetic ability to take control of their reality and relinquish their dependency on the tyrants, an alternate Earth would naturally form, allowing for expression of this new consciousness. The humans who wished to remain under the reign of Marduk and his tyrants would be left to their fate, perhaps to learn independence at another time in some possible future.

The Council asked if any members present wished to speak on behalf of the earthlings, or had any new evidence to present to the court. Inanna's mind raced. What could she say? That Olnwynn had been murdered by his own son, that Atilar had violated a young priestess, that Chandhroma had been poisoned in the harem? It didn't sound good, much less profoundly promising. Earth was so difficult to explain; it was so dense and complicated by its multitudinous polarities. Feeling her mouth suddenly go dry, Inanna stood up to speak anyway.

She couldn't imagine what had come over her, or what she was about to say. But a force had pulled her to her feet and was putting words in her mouth. It was Olnwynn. Somehow he had temporarily gotten control of her consciousness, and for better or worse, was about to speak through her to the entire Council.

"I would speak for the Earth and its people," Olnwynn began. "It may be difficult for you to understand what life on Earth is like. You have never sat in a green forest and listened to the wind. You have not seen the golden silent sun rising over our majestic mountains, or listened to the beating wings of a tiny hummingbird as it drinks nectar from a rose. Humans are not aware of many things as I can see, but they are worthy of your attention and worth saving. Have you never held a helpless baby in your arms, perhaps your own son, and wanted to protect him?"

Melinar pushed Olnwynn aside and continued speaking through Inanna. "The human species is a mixture of all the races that have come to Earth and mated with the life forms who lived there. They are you; they carry the seeds of many of the genetic lines that exist throughout the universe. If given a chance, if given some help, they can be wondrous indeed. I would ask the Etherians to continue to increase the frequency band of *The Wave*."

*The Wave* was a term which described a frequency band the Etherians were emitting toward planet Earth. It carried energies of truth and enlightenment; it carried the power to awaken the dormant genes. If only the sleeping humans could rouse themselves from their dream of limitation and open themselves to this *Wave*, their DNA would automatically mutate and set them free. All they had to do was to turn off the electronic machines that emanated Marduk's frequency web and listen to the sounds of nature, of the forest, of singing rivers and whispering winds.

Inanna told the Council Gracie's story. She gave them the hope that Gracie might make certain choices and make them soon. Inanna knew it was a long shot, and that she was making it all sound better than it was, but it was her only chance. Perhaps Gracie's story might encourage the Etherians to increase the intensity of *The Wave*.

Inanna closed by saying that she truly loved the Earth and the people who inhabited it, and that she and her family were doing all they could to thwart the tyrant manipulators. She beseeched the Council to continue in their assistance. Anu then thanked the Etherians for their protection of Earth and for the asylum they were now giving to Anu and his son, Enlil.

Everyone at the Council understood that there was more riding on this situation than just Earth's inhabitants. It was also understood that if the human species could set itself free, the effects of tyranny which now rippled throughout the entire Pleiadian star system would lessen. Anu and Enlil would then travel back in time to free the leaders of the numerous Pleiadian worlds, and help in the liberation of their homelands from Marduk, his tyrant clones, and the hordes of warrior armies.

It was time for a shift in the balance in the Universe. The forces of light were in readiness to overcome the forces of darkness, for a time. It was the end of the Kali Yuga, the end of a period of play in the mind of Prime Creator.

On the way home, Inanna thought about her man, wondering if he had he seen her. Had he listened when she spoke? Oh, how would she ever meet one such as him? Melinar giggled, flashing his brilliants in the Eye of her Mind, but he didn't say a word. He was saving Inanna's future in a secret place. For now they had better get back to Gracie.

XV

# A BLACK HELICOPTER

Gracie was watching the starry sky from her little cabin. The fire was glowing with warmth and, curled up at her feet, her dogs were dreaming, their paws twitching. Gracie gasped at the beauty of a large shooting star falling across the night sky. She tried to remember what that meant; was it good luck? All she could think of was unidentified flying objects. In 1975 Gracie had seen a UFO for herself on Mount Shasta in California. Not that it was unusual to see UFOs on Mount Shasta; people there saw them all the time. But Gracie had seen her ship in broad daylight, and the experience had stayed with her.

Gracie had been hiking with some friends and had wandered off by herself. She had looked up at the beautiful clear blue sky to see a big pewter-like disc floating above her. Instead of being excited, Gracie had panicked; adrenaline had rushed all through her body. In the very same moment, the ship had ascended straight up and vanished from sight. Gracie had run to her friends, gasping, "Did you see it? Did you see it?" But no one had seen anything. Only Gracie had seen the UFO that day. She could never forget or solve this mystery, and it had haunted her ever since.

Naturally, she had read every book she could find on UFOs and other people's experiences with them, but it didn't seem to help. Many people tried to talk Gracie out of her experience, telling her she just had a vivid imagination, but Gracie knew what she had seen that day and no one could convince her otherwise.

Even stranger were the paintings Gracie had produced years before the UFO sighting, when she was barely six- teen. The paintings were of groups of beings that looked exactly like the gray aliens which later were commonly drawn by many people who claimed to have seen or to have been abducted by them. Gracie was shocked when she had first seen the gray alien beings of her paintings in a popular movie, and then later, one appeared on the cover of a best- selling book. Gracie couldn't remember ever having been abducted, as many others had, even though she tried to find such memories; nor could she find in herself any fear about these little gray friends. Mysteriously, all the paintings Gracie had done from this period were stolen. It was cer- tainly her most popular series.

Finding her eyes a little tired from stargazing, she closed them. In the Eye of her Mind, Gracie found herself flying through space, galaxies whizzing by her; or was it the other way around? Gracie felt herself moving closer toward a particular planet. The colors were very strange, rather like surrealistic computer animation, definitely not Earth colors. The planet was barren, empty of life or living beings, and

Gracie soon tired of the elegantly lonely landscapes there.

Flying back into space, she felt herself resting in what appeared to be her private ship. There was a reclining chair which faced some kind of control board, but everything was dark and dimly lit from within. The ship seemed to operate solely on Gracie's thoughts, and the being she had become, who operated this vehicle, knew exactly how to command it with her mind.

The ship as a material object then mysteriously disappeared from around Gracie, and her consciousness began to move effortlessly through space to explore another planet. This planet had similar colors, but there were great pools of liquid, with beings forming themselves out of these pools. The liquid beings were very gentle and friendly. Gracie felt as though she could stay there a long time and learn from them.

Gracie heard a voice in her head: "It's the Liquidians!" Atilar had been attracted by Gracie's adventure, as this planet was one of his favorites. He was smiling at Gracie and nodding to his friends, the Liquidians, introducing everyone. It was more than Gracie could compute. She sat up with a jolt, spooking her dogs. Gathering her wits about her, she decided it was time to go to bed and get some sleep. Occasionally it all just got too weird and she couldn't handle any more.

Gracie went up to her little bed and snuggled down into the warm covers. Protectively, Olnwynn showed up. Chastising Atilar and accusing him of overloading the poor girl, the great Celtic warrior seated himself at the foot of Gracie's bed between the two pups to stand guard over this night.

Marduk floated in the turquoise waters of his pool in Sri Lanka. He particularly liked this island in the Indian Ocean because, when it was named Ceylon, it had been the home of the Raksasa demon Ravanna, who had given such difficulty to Lord Rama and Sita in an earlier time. Marduk smiled at his memories while watching a rare and colorful tropical bird fly across his sky. He also loved Sri Lanka because it was a trouble-spot, like the Middle East, Northern Ireland, and, more recently, Egypt. All of these troubled areas made delicious eating for Marduk and his armies, who fed off of fear and despair.

An android servant entered Marduk's garden. "Sir, something is coming over the scanner which I feel I must report to you. There is evidence of inter-dimensional consciousness among the earthlings."

"What?" Marduk bolted up from his inflatable float, knocking over his French crystal martini glass. "Follow me to the scanning room," he ordered.

Marduk led the android down to the scanning room; no one ever dared to lead Marduk anywhere. The scanner was in the underground communications center, one of many Marduk had constructed. He had made an art form out of underground architecture. His new state-of-the-art tunneling machines made the old tunnels of the Snake People look crude and pathetic by comparison. Marduk's tunnels were unsurpassed and lined with a material which looked exactly like fine Italian marble, but gave off a wide spectrum of light and electromagnetic frequencies.

The scanner room was furnished with a Louis XIV desk embellished with real gold and a throne chair to match. Antique sedan chairs from China lined the north wall of the room, and a Persian carpet covered the lapis lazuli floor. The scanner was flashing a signal in recognition at the location of the inter-dimensional consciousness. The location was noted: Lost Mountain, the Pacific Northwest.

Marduk was furious. This new consciousness was only beginning, but Marduk knew he had to extinguish it immediately before it grew and spread to others like some heinous cancer. If human beings came to realize that there were other dimensions and other life forms their brains might open beyond the normal pitiful ten-percent capacity, and they could not be controlled. And it was control that Marduk lived for and, in fact, lived off.

Marduk ordered a helicopter to Lost Mountain for the dual purposes of photographing the area and frightening the human living there; perhaps he could frighten her right off the mountain, back into the cities where the electromagnetic frequencies were stronger, more invasive, back into the survival mode which would crush this budding awareness.

Gracie woke. Her dogs were barking frantically. Through her bedroom window, a beam of light was shining a spotlight on the covers of Gracie's bed. The light came from a helicopter hovering loudly outside Gracie's window. She leapt from the bed and ran downstairs. *What on earth?*

There it was—a large black helicopter that did not look like any helicopter she had ever seen before. It was sleek, ominous, threatening, like something out of a science-fiction novel, and its blackness was made more sinister by the aerodynamic body design.

The black machine continued to beam its spotlight into Gracie's little cabin. For a moment she wished for a gun or any kind of weapon with which to defend herself. Oh sure, Gracie, she thought, a lot of good that would do you. Any group with a copter like that would naturally have sophisticated weapons, at least M-16s. Gracie forced herself to breathe deeply. The helicopter flew up and down the valley that Gracie lived very much alone in. It was shining a powerful infrared light over an old abandoned barn and chicken coop down the road from her cabin.

Finally, after intruding its spotlight into the cabin for one last time, the nasty black helicopter flew away, seemingly heading north. It was difficult for Gracie to tell at that point. She sat down exhausted and tried to calm the dogs. It was definitely wine time!

As Gracie ran around her cabin, Olnwynn drew Inanna's attention to the black helicopter.

"Marduk!" Inanna exclaimed. "He has some nerve. If he so much as touches Gracie, I'll have him up before the Council before he can blink. What I wouldn't give to aim my plasma gun at that perfect nose of his!"

Melinar stopped Inanna's thought forms. "Inanna, my dear, we are in the process of evolving here. It is dysfunctional for you to entertain thoughts of revenge at this time."

"I'd like to entertain that reptilian son of a...Okay, Melinar, I'll be good. It's just the Olnwynn in me."

Olnwynn laughed. Now she's going to blame me, he thought, when she created me in the first place. "Inanna, we must protect Gracie," Olnwynn pleaded.

Inanna went to her screens and placed a call to Anu, who was back on the Etherian ships with Enlil. Atilar was finding all this very interesting, and when he saw the Etherian mother ship come into Inanna's consciousness, he excitedly projected himself on board. He was immediately standing beside Anu and Enlil in the communications room as they were being briefed on the helicopter incident.

"Atilar, what are you doing?" cried Inanna.

Anu spoke up for Atilar, "Oh, allow him to remain. I have been wishing to speak with one of your multidimensional selves, Inanna, and this one is suitable enough. Do not worry any further about Gracie; I will arrange protection immediately. That scoundrel, even if he is my grandson, shall not be permitted to destroy what may be our last hope."

"Oh, Anu, don't even say those words, *last hope*. Surely, the multidimensional selves of Enki, Ninhursag, or some of the others are getting close to activating the divine genes?" Inanna sighed.

"Well, it appears to be a matter of synchronicity and synergy, my dear. If only one will awaken, the others who so desire will also awaken simultaneously. The transformation is interconnected. Each human is linked, and thus each is a part of the others. All are vital to our mission."

"I miss you, Anu. Give my great-grandmother, Antu, my love. I am signing off now. Don't let Atilar be a bother."

Anu, in all his majesty and beauty, turned to his son, Enlil. The two were so much alike by nature that even Enlil's golden hair was beginning to gray like Anu's. It had been a difficult time for both leaders. Anu had lost Nibiru, and Enlil had lost Earth. The two, father and son, had spent the last centuries assembling a renegade army to reclaim the Pleiadian star system from Marduk and his tyrants. Working with the Council and many of the Pleiadian leaders who were also in exile, they were planning a return. But, first the wounds that the family of Anu had inflicted on planet Earth had to be healed.

Both Anu and Enlil, along with Enki and the others, had been forced to do a great deal of introspective thinking. They had to come to terms with the adolescent stage of their evolution, and they had to change sufficiently to move beyond tyranny. Anu and Enlil moved toward the door, commanding Atilar to follow them, to meet with the Etherians.

# XVI

# THE MOTHER SHIP

Anu and Enlil, followed by Atilar, entered the central meeting room of the Etherian mother ship. Seated around a large oval table were three Etherians: the captain, the chief engineer, and the communications director. Atilar wondered at the bodies of the Etherians. At first glance they appeared solid, but on closer inspection, it became obvious that they were actually transparent, or perhaps translucent. The physics of their forms could be described as molecules which vibrated at varying rates to give off many different appearances of density. It was as if the Etherians could actually modify their life frequencies and adapt to any level of vibration. The Etherians were more beautiful than any people Atilar had ever seen. Their keen, gentle intelligence gave their faces a structural beauty no human possessed, not even Atilar's unfortunate priestess.

The interior of the ship was clean, elegant, and brilliantly functional. Light emanated from the walls themselves. Here technology and art were perfectly married; Atilar had never seen anything like it. The ship must have measured a great many miles in diameter. Certainly it was much larger than it appeared on Inanna's viewing screen. There were hundreds, perhaps thousands of beings on board.

Anu spoke to the captain. "Sir, the tyrant Lord Marduk has sent a black helicopter to torment one of the Lady Inanna's multidimensional selves. The human in question has shown potential for the future activation of her DNA and has recalled many of her other selves, who have been in communication with one another, as well as with Inanna. I want to put a stop to this harassment. Lord Marduk once again is breaking the Law of Non-Interference. I request a dome of protective light be placed over the area of Lost Mountain, and that the girl herself be monitored by your communications director. We see her as valuable in the process of transformation and the possible future."

"Yes, of course, Anu. It will be seen to immediately." The captain nodded to the communications director and the chief engineer, who then left the room to attend to the protective dome and subsequent monitoring.

"Who is this with you and Enlil?" the captain inquired of Anu.

"This is one of Lady Inanna's multidimensional selves. I believe his name is Atilar. Is that correct?" Anu asked.

Atilar answered, "Yes, that is my name. I am from the time of middle Atlantis, before the great corruption of power which took place there. My life data is basically that of an adept. I sought self-mastery all my life and achieved much greatness, but as I was never allowed to feel, the imbalance drove me to take the virginity of a young priestess I had fallen in love with, and for that crime I was subsequently executed."

The captain looked deeply into Atilar, and with the greatest of compassion said, "My son, it is the way of the lower density frequencies. The intensity of the material rings of Earth and other such places tends to generate unbalanced experiences which often lead to tragedy. These lower density worlds are the places of opportunity for Prime Creator to learn, to test Itself against Itself in the vast illusion of Its separation. You must be as Prime Creator; forgive yourself and absorb the vagaries of your life data. Then you may move on to other worlds to play in the forever."

"But for now," Anu interjected, "we are playing *free the humans from their tyrants.*"

"Yes, I am beginning to understand." Atilar loved being on the mother ship, and he was feeling wonderful. "I would like to stay here with you and learn as much as I can. My background as a modulator of crystal frequency makes me particularly interested in your ship and Etherian technology. Unless, of course, the Lady Inanna should need me or call me. As she is my creator, I still wish to serve her in whatever manner I can."

Anu glanced at the captain for approval. It was the captain's ship and not for Anu to decide. But the captain agreed, saying it would be interesting to have a human from the planet Earth, even a discarnate one, on board. Perhaps they could all learn something from one another, and it was good to explore the human potential with one such as Atilar.

Atilar was very happy; he searched his vocabulary for a way to express his feelings, but he was unable to. The ship itself possessed such a new frequency-level of being that as of yet, Atilar could find no words to express the subtleties of his thoughts.

The captain read Atilar's mind and said, "You have already discovered one of our dilemmas. How do we communicate with beings whose frequency does not resonate with the same subtlety as our own?"

The door opened and a man entered with his arm around an incredibly beautiful woman. The captain introduced the two. "May I present the Lady of the Garnets and her husband, Commander Naemon. They are of the family of Lona, a great dynasty of Pleiadians, who have had the misfortune to be conquered by the one who also torments planet Earth, Lord Marduk. They are here for the same reason as you, Anu and Enlil, to observe the progress of the human species, and to assist wherever they can."

Atilar could not help but stare at the Lady of the Garnets. She was like his priestess in some ways. Her skin was a velvety white that glowed with health; her eyes were emerald green. But it was her long hair that transfixed him, being a deep red with copper highlights. In keeping with her title, she was covered with garnets; they encircled her graceful throat, and were sewn cunningly throughout her garment. She was stunning, and her husband, the commander, was an even match for her beauty, handsome and strong. It was easy to see that he adored her.

Nodding at Anu, whom she obviously already knew, and then looking at Atilar, the Lady of the Garnets spoke. "Who, may I ask, is this charming being?" An earthling, even one without a real body, was somewhat of an anomaly onboard ship, and naturally aroused the Lady's curiosity.

The captain replied, "This is Atilar, recently arrived here from planet Earth. He is one of the Lady Inanna's multidimensional selves, and he has requested to stay on the ship in order to learn."

"One of Inanna's selves? Oh, how exciting," the Lady

responded. "Inanna and I are great friends. I used to attend the parties of her great-grandmother, Antu, on Nibiru, when I was a child. Both Inanna and I were such imaginative, adventurous little girls. We have always been similar in our dispositions. I am so fond of her. I would love to show Atilar around the ship."

She turned to her husband. "Wouldn't that be fun, darling?" Atilar could see that the commander was happy to do whatever this beautiful woman desired.

"Of course, my angel!" The commander squeezed her delicate hand. And so, Atilar joined his new friends for a tour of the Etherian mother ship, while Anu, Enlil, and the Etherian captain went to check on the dome being projected over Lost Mountain in the Pacific Northwest.

Gracie dragged herself out of bed. She hadn't exactly slept last night after the helicopter had departed. She began grinding lots of coffee beans, and the sound of the coffee grinder reminded her of the copter's motors. Good lord, Gracie thought, what was that all about? Mostly, she was just plain angry. How dare they fly over her house like that and shine that damn light in her bedroom! Wasn't there anything she could do?

Gracie sat down by the telephone with a thick, strong cup of dark roast espresso and began to search the Yellow Pages. She called every government agency and airport she could think of. Always, the answer was the same: there were no reported helicopter flights last night, none, zero, zippo. It hadn't happened. Almost everyone put her on hold, then transferred her to some other party. It took forever. She even called the Drug Enforcement Agency. Oh, they were very helpful. They requested that she report back to them if the black helicopter should return to her property; they thought it might be Canadian drug dealers, thank you.

The only person who was at all helpful was a retired airline pilot who worked at one of the small local airports. He told her to forget it, that she would never, unequivocally *never* find out who it was or why they were there. It hadn't happened. He had also said something very odd. Gracie had told him that she knew it wasn't a UFO because it made so much noise, and UFOs were silent. He had unnerved her by answering, "Not all of them!"

By lunchtime Gracie had exhausted all the possibilities. If even the Navy, the Air Force, and the DEA wouldn't help her, why bother. She decided to head for town and get some lunch. Gracie got her dogs into her pickup truck and rumbled down the dirt road, off Lost Mountain, and into the small nearby town. She was tired, hungry, and angry. She hated the idea of not being able to find out who her intruders had been. And what if they came back?

She stopped in to visit some local friends she had made and told them her story. They didn't seem to really believe her. They had probably wondered why an attractive young woman like Gracie would want to live all alone up on Lost Mountain; they figured there must be something funny about her. They were kind, but had no help to offer. Gracie knew that, as usual, she was alone.

When Gracie returned to her cabin, she saw there were messages for her on her telephone's answering machine. For a minute she felt hopeful. Maybe someone had called her back with some information. Gracie pushed the play button: there were no voices, only a totally unfamiliar sound. Gracie listened carefully, trying to identify the noise. It was so weird, like—well, what *was* it like? Sort of a sewing-machine sound echoing in a huge amphitheater, or the whirring of soft engines. It sounded like—well, yes, it sounded like the inside of a giant spaceship. But how could Gracie know what *that* was? Somehow she did; somehow she knew she was listening to the sounds that came from inside a ship, a ship somewhere in outer space.

The strange sounds continued for the entire tape; a long time. Gracie felt much better. That night as she slept, she dreamed that her small valley was covered by an invisible dome of energy which protected her and the dogs from any and all intruders. The dome came from an enormous starship far out in space, somewhere beyond Saturn. Covered with this light of love from far above planet Earth, Gracie slept soundly and peacefully.

Inanna and Melinar smiled from the transparent oval deep within the Earth. It was nice to have friends in high places.

# XVII

# A MERGING

The following morning, Gracie went to the cedar forest. It was one of those days that can come to the Pacific Northwest any time of the year, spring or winter. On the East Coast, this sort of day was called Indian summer. The sun was shining and warm, the sky brilliantly clear blue, and a sharp, cool breeze gently played with the cedars, causing the sunlight to dance through the trees and their pale green needles. Dust and mist rose from the forest floor in magical wisps.

Gracie lay down on a thick bed of star moss and felt the strength of the Earth. She relaxed into the feeling of knowing she was getting close to her true home, the home within. Her dogs settled themselves around her in their usual protective manner, both happily smiling to be in such a wonderful place. It was as if they sensed something special was about to occur, and Gracie laughed to see them so joyful.

Gracie looked around the forest and saw Inanna standing beside a great old tree. Gracie had come to love and trust this beautiful wise lady with her warm blue skin, who now stood lovingly watching Gracie and her pups. It was a beautiful day, a day that reminded Inanna of happier times when her life had been so simple, when she had been the spoiled and adored child of the family of Anu. Melinar was with Inanna, his brilliants flashing.

Inanna focused on the radiant Light Being who had come to her in the Oval of the old Serpent Woman, and evoked that Being into the cedar forest, into this dimension and time. Before Gracie's eyes, the most beautiful Being she had ever seen took form. This Light Being was made up of colorful radiant lights, a spectrum of different colors of gold, iridescent blues and pinks, all shooting as if they were photons unceasingly rearranging themselves for their own pleasure. Just watching the display took Gracie's breath away; she felt tears of joy run down her face. Melinar was exploding with energy, and Inanna felt an unusual peace and contentment.

Gracie asked, "Who are you?"

The radiant Light Being began to speak in a melodious voice that resounded with the harmonies of angelic realms. "I am you, Gracie, and I am Inanna, and all she has ever been, all of her selves. I am Olnwynn and Atilar, I am Sky Maiden and Chandhroma, I am all the expressions that have come from the mind of Prime Creator through me, and through my beloved Inanna."

Gracie started to doubt her own eyes and ears. Surely, Gracie thought, I would never be as sublimely beautiful or as wondrous as this Being who stands before me.

The Being answered Gracie's thoughts. "My sweet child, I am that which you have always been. Remember who you are, remember who we are, Inanna and I. Do not judge yourself. When you judge, you remove yourself from us. We do not judge. We remember, we are, and have always been one: one being, one body. Remember."

Gracie then felt fear come over her body, fear of the unknown. Once again, the Being spoke into Gracie's heart. "I am that which you have always been, Beloved. You need have no fear. Your circuitry is now in alignment for better reception. Surrendering your fear programming will open you up to new possible realities, and give us permission to transmit a wave of change into your very being, into your cells themselves. But you must open yourself, you must allow us to assist you. We cannot go where we are not invited, we cannot interfere unless you request us to assist you to wash away the limited programming of your genetic codes. We desire to become consciously one with you."

Gracie looked at Inanna, who was obviously deliriously happy, and Melinar, who appeared to be spinning faster than the speed of light. There was a soft golden light in the forest; and everything which normally appeared solid was pulsating with light and seemingly translucent. Or was everything truly never solid, but merely vibrating light energy?

The Being again spoke. "You see matter as vibrating energy, because that is what it is. Delete your fear programming, beloved. Fear and doubt are circuitbreakers, love is a circuit-enhancer, an amplifier. We are Love, the Love of Prime Creator. Open to us and let go of your fear. Your life and its expressions will become expanded beyond any dream you have known.

"You were never separate from us, Beloved. You are in us, and we are in you. Like those little Russian dolls which nest one within the other, we are all a part of one another.

At times many of the other multidimensional selves began to remember, but it is now, in this time and space, that you, Gracie, are beginning the process of unifying all the experiences of Inanna's projected selves. All of the life data from the various selves is coming into you in this *now* because you have sought truth, and the time is ripe. The courage and passion of all those who are within you will activate that which has been dormant in your genetic codes, and will radiate out onto the planet in a contagious joy."

A gentle breeze caressed Gracie's face as she became aware of the tears streaming down her cheeks. She had never been so happy in all of her life. It was as if all the pain she carried within her was washed away, while something new had been born in its place. Gracie felt loved, and the power of that love began to start a nuclear reaction in her entire metabolic system. Gracie felt as if her cells were exploding, bubbling within her. It wasn't like anything she had ever experienced before.

She looked around and saw that the forest had filled up with beings, only some of whom she knew as Inanna's multidimensional selves, or as Gracie's so-called past lives, which really weren't past at all, because as Gracie could plainly see, they were all here, right now. And they were merging into her while still remaining their separate selves.

She looked at Olnwynn, the wonderful old Celtic warrior, still handsome, grinning from ear to ear. She heard him give his wild banshee war cry, and felt his courage melt into her. Chandhroma danced in front of Gracie; the silver bells encircling her delicate ankles sang in delight. Chandhroma's graceful, fluid movements inspired Gracie to remember what her own name meant: grace. Her mother had given her that name because, as her mother had always said, like grace, Gracie had come from God's loving mercy. Even in the midst of her own personal unhappiness, Gracie's mother had tried to love her and had given her invaluable gifts. Such thoughts made Gracie cry. Life could hurt so much.

Atilar walked toward Gracie and entered into her being. He was eager to return to the mother ship, but he knew that this moment was more important. Atilar had mastered focus, and his knowledge of the variation of power frequencies in crystals had many other potential applications. Gracie absorbed his understanding and the wisdom Atilar had gained from his fall. Atilar still loved the young priestess with all his heart, and he had determined to find her somewhere in the vast expanse of time, intending to help her in any way he could.

Sky Maiden came forth. She was so at home in this forest, she who loved the Earth and the sky, who had become one with the heavens to bring forth its blessings onto Earth, to field and forest. Sky Maiden blessed Gracie, and gave her the wisdom of her life as an Indian girl. It was a most natural union for these two; the blood of Sky Maiden's tribe still flowed in Gracie's veins. Gracie felt herself absorb the life data of Sky Maiden, her love of the heavens, and her lost love, Flame Feather—the sadness of loss and the passion for life.

Each of Inanna's selves dissolved into Gracie's consciousness, each bringing gifts. Merwyn brought his patience and love of learning, Rachael her innocent purity, and Tenzin his artistic and mystical visions. Gracie was filled, her body was on fire; *the fire that burns, but does not consume.* Inanna touched Gracie's face lovingly and vanished into the forest mist. The others also vanished; some were not Inanna's multidimensional selves and were only there to observe. Gracie had never seen them before and did not know who they were. To her amazement, there had been a beautiful woman with flowing red hair, who was covered in garnets. Gracie would have to remember to ask Inanna who this lady was, but not now. Gracie was beginning to feel a little tired and very hungry, and it was time to go home.

The dogs leapt up to return home. Their thoughts on chicken soup and warm buttered bread, they led Gracie down the wandering trail back to her cabin. What a day, she thought. What a wonderful, magical, amazing day! Gracie wondered if this was what bliss was like.

# XVIII

# STARDUST

Marduk sat in the master control room watching the scanner monitor energy sources. The population of Earth continuously produced the necessary requirements for Marduk and his legions to nourish themselves: fear, guilt, and anxiety, the subtle energies on which his troops were fed. Marduk was expecting some champagne and caviar to be served to him, so when the door opened, he was a little surprised at the expression on the face of his empty-handed servant.

"Master, a protective dome of high-frequency light has been placed over the area known as Lost Mountain. We are not certain of the source, but we believe it comes from an Etherian mother ship located somewhere beyond the orbit of the planet Saturn."

Marduk felt his reptilian adrenaline surge through his

body. How dare they? Those damned Etherians would not so easily block his reconnaissance mission. He would send a few of his fighter ships to counteract the protective dome. Two or three quick blasts of radiation from his plasma weapons would easily destroy the dome.

Marduk gave the orders and called for his champagne. Sitting back down in front of the scanners, he once again cursed the Etherians—something one simply doesn't do.

It was night on Lost Mountain. The skies were crystal-clear, and Gracie was feeling like—well, there aren't really any words to describe her feelings. Lighting the candles in the cabin, she sat down near the window and looked out into the night. She thought, everything looks so different. It's as if I never even saw the stars before.

Gracie wondered how Inanna had begun to take her multidimensional journey. Inanna activated her focus, and called forth the first of her flesh-and-blood excursions, the white-robed being who had brought a column of light to the seekers in the Himalayas. She showed Gracie the circle, and allowed her to feel the powerful love that being had come to feel for those in the circle. Inanna had given of herself and had grown to love them dearly. And because we become what we love, she became a part of them. Nurturing them had been the most fulfilling experience she had known up until that time.

"All the beings in that circle," Inanna explained, "have been the source of the love which has generated so much passion in all my multidimensional selves. And some in the circle are the very people my selves have loved and interacted with in time and space."

Gracie saw Inanna as the white-robed being who had loved so deeply that she had dared to descend into the denser frequencies of Earth time in human bodies. Gracie felt no fear as she saw waves of energy coming from the hands within the white robes. Tenderly moving toward her, these waves of pulsating light permeated her with a lightness of being. Gracie opened up.

In the Eye of her Mind, Gracie saw the mutating brilliants in all their flashing colors. Her body temperature was increasing, and as the waves washed over her, every cell in her body began to vibrate with greater frequency and turn into light itself. Gracie was becoming light: not reflected light, but light from its own source, within.

Gracie felt herself spreading out, expanding into the Universe. She remembered all of Inanna's selves, Olnwynn, Sky Maiden, Tenzin, and the others. They all came to her and smiled because they were in her and a part of her becoming; what she experienced, so did they. Gracie felt a oneness, not only with the selves, but a oneness with Inanna, and beyond that, with the Earth, the tall cedars, the stars, and the Universe. Gracie transformed into an inexpressible feeling of joy as she knew, simply *knew* that she was one with all life, everything. She became Joy itself.

Gracie began to laugh. A gentle loving laughter encompassed her and, as laughter is contagious, Inanna began to laugh with her. The two girls were laughing and laughing and laughing and...

Inanna and Gracie began to have a new feeling. At the same moment they both realized that because they felt they were one with everything in creation, they were also one with, yes, one with Marduk himself. Not only was he a part of them, but they loved him. Incredibly, Inanna felt love for Marduk, she even saw his beauty, and that love gave Inanna and Gracie the wisdom to know that not only was Marduk the unconscious projection of the tyrannical folly of the children of Anu, but Marduk was also a part of Prime Creator.

Marduk was the portion of the energy which allowed the magical play of an illusion of limitation to take place on Earth in the human species in order to build up enough energy to create an entire new life form, a new genetic code which carried new possibilities and fresh potentials for creation.

The gentle laughter of Inanna and Gracie rang out across the Earth and into the heavens. The force of their joy was simultaneously spreading out over the planet and beyond. There are no barriers on consciousness, and many of the others who had sought truth were having the same experience, at the exact same moment. The multidimensional selves of Enki and Ninhursag, as well as the other members of the family of Anu, all began to laugh. There were also many others caught in the contagion of truth, people who were from other life forms and earthlings alike; all were laughing in their newfound knowledge. The process had begun. The truth had set them free.

Marduk spilled his champagne. A terrible vision confronted him. On the screens of his energy-monitoring scanners, there was suddenly evidence of a large drop in productivity. In less than an Earth minute, the supply of fear had dwindled dismally. Marduk sprang up from his golden throne and stubbed his toe—well, his claw.

There must be some mistake; his vast supply of resources could not have vanished so quickly. He began to shriek at his servants and to push all sorts of electronic alarm buttons. Marduk was freaking out, actually; his eyes were bulging and his face became contorted. He waved his arms wildly in the air and screamed at his clones. But Gracie and all the others like her were beyond him. Marduk could no longer influence or harm them, because they had mutated their genetic codes and moved out of his frequency. They were vibrating in a spectrum he could not even see, much less touch.

Atilar had returned to the mother ship, and was with the commander and his Lady of the Garnets. They were all very excited by what was happening on planet Earth. The Lady had decided to project multidimensional selves into various time/space coordinates to join in on the fun with her friend, Inanna. Of course, the commander would join her; he was so protective of his beloved woman. A trend had begun, and many more would follow.

Back on Lost Mountain, Gracie glanced at the clock. It was almost four o'clock in the morning, and still dark outside. The stars were just beginning to fade. Gracie was full of energy and thinking it would be great to go for a ride. Throwing a few essentials in her backpack, Gracie called her dogs, and they all went out to get in her pickup truck. As they bumped down the dusty road that led off the mountain, Gracie mused about how good it would be to ride down the open road in the middle of the night, feeling the wind in her hair.

Yes, Gracie thought, I'll head toward the city, any city

will do, and maybe from there I'll move on to another, carrying *The Wave* within me, offering it, just by being there, to anyone who wants it. Under her breath, she started to hum a few bars from that old Civil War gospel tune, *Amazing Grace*.

Gracie's dogs vied for the window. They shared her happiness, and they were always ready for adventure. As they moved down the dirt road, Gracie's truck kicked up dust; but tonight, it was stardust.

# XIX

# AFTER

It was time for a meeting with the Council of the Intergalactic Federation. Inanna and Anu were to attend with the other family members—Enki, Ninhursag, Ninurta, Ereshkigal, and all the rest, excluding Marduk. Inanna was flushed with excitement; she had so many things to report. Her multidimensional selves were, at last, coming along so well, and real change was in its beginnings, thanks to *The Wave* and so many other factors. She must remember to thank the Etherians for protecting Gracie. Inanna was exhilarated with the happiness that comes from accomplishment, and the new sense of oneness and love she and Gracie had discovered. Life was good, and Inanna looked more beautiful than ever. She felt wonderful; her soft blue skin was glowing.

Even Enlil had complimented Inanna and, of course,

Anu had given her a big kiss. Bless his heart, he had always loved his Inanna. Antu was there also. She wasn't about to miss out on all the excitement, or the opportunity to meet new friends to invite to her parties. This was a festive occasion.

Anu and Enlil were prepared to discuss the possibilities for moving the exiled leaders back into the Pleiadian star system. There was still a long way to go, but the writing was on *The Wall*, so to speak, and Enlil was already planning the logistics of such an operation. The iron grip of tyranny was loosening throughout the galaxies. It was the time for a new golden age to begin, and for the Kali Yuga, the age of darkness, to be finished. Prime Creator was, as always, moving on.

Inanna stood alone watching the others in the Intergalactic Hall. She was filled with happiness, and wasn't really thinking about anything whatsoever, when she felt a presence behind her. A warm feeling spread over her, and she thought she felt someone breathing very close to her.

Slowly, Inanna turned around in response to this subtle energy which was beginning to command her total attention. There he was, the wonderful man she had so wanted to meet for such a long time. Inanna met his eyes; they danced with wisdom and humor, and were as diamonds in her night. She felt a deep recognition, but did not know why. Silence overwhelmed Inanna.

He reached his hand out toward hers and, smiling, spoke. "Allow me to introduce myself."

Sources for *Inanna Returns*

*Abduction: Human Encounters with Aliens*, by John Mack; Scribner's Sons, 1994.

*Alien Identities: Ancient Insights into Modern UFO Phenomena*, by Richard Thompson; Govardhan Hill Publishing, 1993.

*Babylon*, Revised Edition by Joan Oates; Thames and Hudson, 1979.

*Bringers of the Dawn: Teachings from the Pleiadians*, by Barbara Marciniak; Bear & Co., 1992.

*Flying Serpents and Dragons*, by R.A. Boulay; Galaxy Books, 1990.

*Gilgamesh, translated from the Sin-leqi-unninni version*, by John Gardner and John Maier; Alfred A. Knopf, 1984.

*The Greatest Story Never Told*, by Lana Corrine Cantrell; Biohistorical Press, 1988.

*The Holographic Universe*, by Michael Talbot; Harper Collins, 1991.

*Inanna, Queen of Heaven and Earth: Her Stories and Hymns from Sumer*, by Diane Wolkstein and Samuel Noah Kramer; Harper and Row, 1983.

*The Language of the Gods: Sanskrit Keys to India's Wisdom*, by Judith M. Tyberg; East West Cultural Center, 1970.

*The Mahabharata*, translated and edited by J.A.B. van Buitenen; University of Chicago Press, 1973.

*The Myth of the Goddess: Evolution of an Image*, by Anne Baring and Jules Cashford; Arkana Penguin Books, 1991.

*Myths and Symbols in Indian Art and Civilization*, by Heinrich Zimmer; Bollingen Series/Princeton University Press, 1946.

*Quantum Reality: Beyond the New Physics*, by Nick Herbert; Anchor Press/Doubleday, 1985.

*Samuel Taylor Coleridge, The Oxford Poetry Library*, edited by H.J. Jackson; Oxford University Press, 1994.

*The Secret Garden*, by Mahmud Shabistari, translated by Johnson Pasha; The Octagon Press, London, 1969.

*Sexual Personae. Art and Decadence from Nefertiti to Emily Dickinson*, by Camille Paglia; Yale University Press, 1990.

*The Sumerians*, by C. Leonard Woolley; W.W. Norton & Co., 1965.

*The Way of Life, According to Lao Tzu*, translated by Witter Bynner; The Putnam Publishing Group, 1986.

*The Way of The White Clouds: A Buddhist Pilgrim in Tibet*, by Lama Anagarika Govinda; Shambhala, 1966.

*When God Was A Woman*, by Merlin Stone; A Harvest/HBJ Book, 1978.

*Wholeness and the Implicate Order*, by David Bohm; Ark Paperbacks, 1983.

Books by Alain Danielou:

*The Gods of India: Hindu Polytheism*; Inner Traditions International Ltd., 1985.

*While the Gods Play: Shiva Oracles and Predictions on the Cycles of History and the Destiny of Mankind*; Inner Traditions International Ltd., 1985.

*YOGA: Mastering the Secrets of Matter and the Universe*; Inner Traditions International Ltd., 1991.

Books by Alain Danielou, cont'd:

*Gods of Love and Ecstasy: the Traditions of Shiva and Dionysus;* Inner Traditions International Ltd., 1979.

*The Complete Kama Sutra,* translated by Alain Danielou; Park Street Press, 1994.

Books by Samuel Noah Kramer:

*History Begins at Sumer: Thirty-Nine Firsts in Man's Recorded History;* University of Pennsylvania Press, 1981.

*In the World of Sumer: an Autobiography;* Wayne State University Press, 1986.

*The Sumerians: Their History, Culture and Character;* University of Chicago Press, 1963.

Books by Doris Lessing:

*Briefing for a Descent Into Hell,* 1971.

*Canopus in Argos—Archives*

　　*Re: Colonized Planet 5, Shikasta,* 1979.

　　*The Marriages between Zones Three, Four, and Five,* 1980.

　　*The Sirian Experiments,* 1980.

　　*The Making of the Representative for Planet 8,* 1982.

　　*The Sentimental Agent in the Volyen Empire,* 1983.

(all Vintage books.)

Books by Zecharia Sitchin:

*The 12th Planet,* 1976.

*The Wars of Gods and Men,* 1985.

*The Stairway to Heaven,* 1980.

(all Avon books.)

# INANNA RETURNS

Please send me _____ copy (ies)

I have enclosed a check or
money order for $_____

My mailing address is:

_____

_____

_____

_____

For extra copies of Inanna Returns, send a check or
money order in the amount of $14.00 (which
includes shipping and handling) to:
Thel Dar Publishing Co.
10002 Aurora Ave. North, #3392
Seattle, Washington 98133-9334